# FOREWORD

Young Writers was established in 1991 with the aim of promoting creative writing in children, to make reading and writing poetry fun.

Once again, this year proved to be a tremendous success with over 41,000 entries received nationwide.

The Zodiac competition has shown us the high standard of work and effort that children are capable of today. The competition has given us a vivid insight into the thoughts and experiences of today's younger generation. It is a reflection of the enthusiasm and creativity that teachers have injected into their pupils, and it shines clearly within this anthology.

The task of selecting poems was a difficult one, but nevertheless, an enjoyable experience. We hope you are as pleased with the final selection in *Zodiac East Sussex* as we are.

# ZODIAC

## *EAST SUSSEX*

Edited by Donna Samworth

First published in Great Britain in 2002 by
*YOUNG WRITERS*
Remus House,
Coltsfoot Drive,
Peterborough, PE2 9JX
Telephone (01733) 890066

HB ISBN 0 75433 574 7
SB ISBN 0 75433 575 5

# CONTENTS

| | |
|---|---|
| Katherine Reilly | 67 |
| Zak Pooley | 67 |
| Claudia Thomas | 68 |
| Nicky Ellis | 68 |
| David Randall | 69 |
| Kirstie Leeves | 69 |
| Anthony Matsell | 70 |
| Victoria Fletcher | 70 |
| Rebecca Vine | 71 |
| Callum Kirk | 71 |
| Tristan Shortland | 72 |
| Catherine Miller | 73 |
| Matthew Payne | 73 |
| Matthew Roberts | 74 |
| Martin Scott | 74 |
| Ben Evans | 75 |
| Dani Ford | 75 |
| Emily Malins | 76 |
| Linda Mileman | 76 |
| Charles McKie | 77 |
| Magnus White | 78 |
| Emma Hale | 78 |
| Calvin Foster | 79 |
| Emily Dudley | 79 |
| Petro Turton | 80 |
| Lucy Saunders | 80 |
| Debbie Vince | 81 |
| Sophie Atkinson | 81 |
| Samantha Bayly | 82 |
| Dan Bates | 82 |
| Jack Farley | 83 |
| David R Thompson | 83 |
| Kirsten Read | 84 |
| Sarah Sheriden | 84 |
| Matthew Brooker | 85 |
| Jodi Males | 86 |
| Kerrie Wickham | 86 |
| Nicola Milton | 87 |

| | |
|---|---|
| Gabrielle Stern | 87 |
| Helen Miller | 88 |
| Rachael Hemsley | 89 |
| Matthew Farmer | 90 |
| Aran Caldwell | 90 |
| Matthew Dalton | 91 |
| Anna Holoway | 92 |
| Katie Holmes | 92 |
| Simon Gayton | 93 |
| Rebecca Dryer | 94 |
| Michael Lynch | 94 |
| Jenny Partridge | 95 |
| Lucinda Palmer | 96 |
| Samantha Holmes | 96 |
| Joe Randall | 97 |
| David Radford | 98 |
| Elea Prior | 98 |
| Felicity Green | 99 |
| Deborah Blanch | 100 |
| Darrel Harris | 100 |
| Clara Tsang | 101 |
| Charley Burgess | 102 |
| Andrew Burnett | 102 |
| Lily Davis | 103 |
| Samantha Edmeads | 104 |
| Oliver Kench | 104 |
| Claire Ashdown | 105 |
| Bronwyn Powell | 106 |
| Lynsey Coleman | 106 |
| Dominic Cranfield | 107 |
| Sophie Jupp | 108 |
| Jonathan Parker | 108 |

Northease Manor School

| | |
|---|---|
| Helena Cole | 109 |
| Helen Hurst | 109 |
| Elliott Hutchings | 110 |
| Edward Harvey | 110 |

# The Poems

# THE LISTENERS

The traveller returned to the lone house,
The sky was darker than a shadowy floor.
The squeaky door opened,
The traveller was stunned by what he saw.
He looked around the funereal house,
It was all dishevelled and cluttered,
Then he found the spine-chilling stairs.
The skirting was shambolic and shattered.
The traveller walked up the tread,
Perplexed and sluggish.
When he reached the top of the murky blur,
All that could be found was chaos and rubbish.
The traveller walked into the first bedroom
And saw a ghost-like figure.
He looked closely at the calm phantom
And stealthily pulled the trigger.
'I kept my word, Father,' he whispered
As he fell towards the phantom ghost.
Then the traveller slowly started to fade away.
Strangely, he joined the phantom host.

*Sam Pullen  (10)*


# HOW TO ENTER YOUR SISTER'S ROOM

Enter your sister's room and make a big mess,
Enter your sister's room and throw her dress.

Enter your sister's room and tip her make-up,
Enter your sister's room, get her Coke and shake it up.

Don't enter your sister's bedroom with her lipstick,
Don't enter your sister's room with a Pritt Stick.

*Don't enter your sister's bedroom!*

*Joanna Henson  (10)*

# LIFE

I can see the sea,
Sea that I dream,
Dream in bed at night,
Night is dark with no light,
Light that can't be seen,
Seen nowhere near me.

I can hear the howl,
Howl from the darkest woods,
Woods with no trees,
Trees that are not really there,
There are no woods,
Woods are in my mind.

I can smell flowers,
Flowers all around us,
Us is me and you,
You are my friend,
Friend is what I need,
Need is the help I have to have.

I can feel the pain,
Pain I don't want,
Want and wanting is nothing,
Nothing is a place out there
Beneath the stars and the sun,
Sun that scorches the earth,
Earth that I live on,
On and on I live!

I can taste the wickedness,
Wickedness of the world,
World which I was placed on,
On and on, it gets older
And I grow older quicker,
Quicker than an old man walks,
Walk, talk, sing and dance
Are only some of
The great gifts of life.

*Danielle Lawson  (11)*


## WHEN DEATH CAME

I was working
On the 100th floor.
I saw an aeroplane,
It crashed into the building.
I was scared,
I ran to the lift,
It was broken.
I ran to the stairs,
I ran down them,
It was too late,
I was stuck.
The gravel
Fell
On to me.

I was freed
By a firefighter.
Why did it happen?
President Bush was very angry.
I was happy I was alive.

*Melissa Doherty  (14)*
*Downs Park School*

## WORLD TRADE CENTER

I was working
On the first floor.
I heard an
Aeroplane.
I was
Escaping
Out of the
World
Trade
Tower.
People were
Running.
On the
Way out of
The building, I saw
The tower falling
Down.
People were
Screaming,
The people
Were running,
People were
Shaking,
And there were
Deaths.

*Kelly Barnett (16)*
*Downs Park School*


## VAMPIRE PET

Take a dog's head
Add dark blue eyes and sharp black teeth.
Add rabbit's ears,
Add crab's legs.

Decorate with colours red and green
And cover with slime.
Cook for ten hours
And you have made my monster.

*Kimberley McClelland  (15)*
*Downs Park School*


## THE LIFT

I was just getting out of the elevator
And the whole building shook.
There were lots of people,
Screaming,
Shouting
And running,
From what
I didn't know,
Yet.
The stairs were
Overcrowded,
Walking in
S
  I
    N
      G
        L
          E
        F
      I
    L
E
I am one of the lucky ones,
I got out.

*Anthony Anslow  (15)*
*Downs Park School*

## THE LAST FLIGHT

I am on the third floor of the World Trade Tower
When a plane crashes in.
People start running and shouting
And trying to get out.
The towers are up in flames.
People who get out are all confused
Wanting to know what is going on.
The fire engines are coming, then
The police and ambulances.
The towers are still in flames.
People who are still in the towers
Are starting to jump.
Then the towers just come down
Like a pack of cards.

The next day there is dust and
Rubble all over the place.
Firefighters are trying to get the
People out from under the bricks.
It's quiet and only one is brought out.
Tony Blair is horrified at
What has happened.
All the firefighters are very tired,
Cold, dusty and hungry.
People are walking around dazed,
Confused, not knowing what to do.
Why the World Trade Centre?
Why kill all those innocent people?
Why did it happen?
It never should have happened.

*Maria French (14)*
*Downs Park School*

# BOMBING IN AMERICA

World Trade Towers - gone,
People are sad and angry.
Why?
Why did it happen?
The poor people on the plane die.
Why?
Why did they do it?
Did they do it for their leader?
Why?
The poor people,
Lost . . . families, husbands and kids.
Why?
Did they deserve it?
No.
The people are shocked.
Other people are jumping.
Why?
To die quicker
So they do not get burnt by the fire?
The fire brigade are risking their lives
To save the trapped people.
Why?
To get more people out before the Towers
Come crashing down.
Why?
The people are sad, heartbroken,
So is America and everyone
Around the world.

*Karl Meredith (15)*
*Downs Park School*

## HALLOWE'EN

A very silent house,
Silent as anything,
No sound,
No light,
Just a silent house,
Very dark and dingy.
I walked through the door,
The door creaked.
The door slammed behind me,
I saw shadows on the wall,
Up on the ceilings,
Everywhere.

*Jamie Vickery (15)*
*Downs Park School*


## DANIEL WOOD

D   aring,
A   mbitious,
N   oisy,
I    mpatient,
E   ncouraging,
L   oving.

W   onderful,
O   utgoing,
O   bliging,
D   ependable.

*Daniel Wood (15)*
*Downs Park School*

## OPEN OCEAN

I dived in,
Taking one breath
Out of my snorkel,
So bubbles went up.
I saw a swarm of sardines,
I put my hand out
And touched a silky body.
Then a whale swam past,
Swallowing the fish in its way.
I saw jellyfish
Flashing like a disco,
I could hardly believe my eyes.
Unluckily, my air had run out,
I had to go up.

*Benjamin Wark  (11)*
*Heathfield Community College*


## THE NONSENSE POEM

I saw a house drop rain,
I saw a cloud in lots of pain,
I saw a patient taller than the house,
I saw a giant being eaten by a mouse
I saw a piece of cheese, greener than green,
I saw a balloon with sharp teeth looking mean,
I saw a fish stamping on people,
I saw an elephant with a big steeple.
I saw a church looking rather fat,
I saw a caterpillar chasing a cat.
I saw a dog buried in a mound,
I saw a bone burn to the ground.

*Hannah Miller  (12)*
*Heathfield Community College*

## MY POEM

Thousands of people in the buildings,
People watch as a plane circles the first building,
It hits.
People on the ground stare in fascination, wondering why?
The black smoke bellows out of the windows,
People in the second building stare at the other,
As a plane crashes into it . . .

Watching the rain, pitter-patter on the patio,
Thinking how wet it must be out there.
The rain looks sad,
As though it knows the thing that I don't want to know.
I sit there watching it pour down,
He's asking me a question,
But what is it?
I continue watching it pour down,
The person next to me nudges me.

He looks angry,
I explain I was thinking of something,
He asks the question again
And I answer it correctly.
Astonished, his face reminds me of the rain,
I get back to watching it pitter-patter down,
It reminds me of what I watched on the
Television, the day before.

Agony on the faces of the men and women on the ground,
People running out of the buildings,
Fire crews arrive,
'Run,' people shout, 'it's going to go.'
The second building collapses
Under the debris, thousands of bodies trapped.

The first one starts to go,
The choking dust clouds over the streets of Manhattan,
From space you can see the devastation of
Where the buildings once stood.
What a dreadful horror!

*Becky Rowe  (13)*
*Heathfield Community College*


## SEPTEMBER 11TH

The bell rings, we pack up and leave,
Joining all the people in the corridor,
Charging to our next lesson like wildebeest.
No panic, no stress, an everyday routine . . .

People's mouths drop.
A plane disappears into a tower. A terrible accident.
A ball of fire bursts from the top.
It can't be! A second plane explodes into the second tower.
People jump, instead of being burnt alive.
All around there is panic as the building falls,
From the sky to the ground.
In slow motion, it collapses into itself,
Hundreds of floors fall, bringing the world to a halt
In a huge pile of rubble.
People rush away from the wave of dust,
Shouting for friends and family, they are soon engulfed by it.
As the dust clears, everything is white, as if a blizzard has hit.
Everyone shared the horror, unable to take their eyes off the TV.

Too much homework.
Leaving the corridors empty and quiet.
On the bus home, thinking I've got it bad,
Not knowing the terror. The horror. The tragedy.

*Tom Clennett  (13)*
*Heathfield Community College*

# THE BROKEN BUILDING

Underneath the shivering trees,
Next to the rusty gate,
Is a winding path leading to
A place that looks out of date.

There's a plaque with special inscription,
That's covered with ivy and moss,
No one can read it these days,
The writing's gone and lost.

The door is off its hinges,
The wallpaper's thin and peeled,
But wait, there's a door not broken,
But it's all closed up and sealed.

You open it slowly and gently,
There's a bright light coming from within,
The room inside's all tidy,
As neat as a brand new pin.

It's a hall for dancing classes,
Children filled this space,
Ballet, tap and modern,
With style, poise and grace.

The children are filing in now,
Memories from the past,
Suddenly you are among them,
How long will this encounter last?

You can't help dancing with them,
You join in with their games,
Then it all disappears so quickly,
Who were they? What were their names?

The room's become old and murky,
Just like it was before,
The children and the teachers
Are not there any more.

There's a presence of ghostly figures,
You can feel it more and more,
But they won't be seen ever again,
Only you know what it was before.

*Megan Axford  (14)*
*Heathfield Community College*


# BEYOND THE GATE

I opened the creaky gate,
Head collar in hand.
With the prick of an ear,
The horses looked up
From their feast on the ground.

With the shake of a bucket
And the click of teeth,
My big, handsome horse
Galloped towards me,
As fast as the speed of light.

With the pounding of hooves
And the whinnying of joy,
Came a big cloud of dust
As he came to a grinding halt,
So pleased to see me.

I felt so warm inside,
My heart glowing,
Like a candle in the dark.

*Rachel Cullimore  (12)*
*Heathfield Community College*

## UNTITLED

At school, geography, lesson five,
We're learning how to tell if a country's developed.
It seems pointless to me,
Who cares how many people there are in the USA,
But then we don't really think about it, do we?

Men and women start the day as usual,
Not knowing what is to be ahead of them.
Smoke surrounds the buildings and the streets.
Still not knowing what has really happened,
If it was an accident, or an act of terrorism.
People from all around the world
Eagerly watching their televisions.

When the second plane circles around the tower,
People look certain this isn't an accident.
The thousands of people try to get in touch with their loved ones,
As they don't know if they are alive or not.
No one in the world can say how much
This has changed everything.

The bell's just gone.
We go for a one minute silence,
Which turns out to be three minutes silence,
Then we carry on as normal.
How can we ever be normal again?

*Rachel Strange (13)*
*Heathfield Community College*


## AUTUMN

Trees rustling in the wind,
Golden leaves fall swiftly off them.
Squirrels racing, gathering nuts,
Getting ready for the winter that follows.

The afternoon sky is lit up by the amber sun,
Horses are cantering round their fields.
Deer and stags run through the forest,
Bronze leaves fall to the ground.

*Alexandra Gill  (11)*
*Heathfield Community College*

## SEPTEMBER 11TH

I arrive at school. Ten minutes until the bell
So I walk around talking to my friends.
Five minutes, school is slowly creeping upon us.
I keep walking. The bell rings . . .

Sirens blare out loud, people scream,
Firefighters trying to help. One after another, people fall;
They never seem to hit the ground,
Falling further and further down.
The screams as the buildings collapse . . .

'Wake up!' the teacher roared at me like a lion,
'Are you listening?' he asked. I didn't reply, just kept quiet.
I stare out of the window and see the steam rise from the wet ground.
Like smoke . . .

A great ball of smoke, dust and debris
Slithers its way along the New York streets like a snake,
Swallowing everything in its path.
People run away down the streets,
Some hide in buildings or behind cars.
Complete devastation . . .

The bell rings for the last time today.
We leave, only to come back tomorrow.

*John Bridgeman  (13)*
*Heathfield Community College*

# THE WALK

When Nathan and I take my brown dog for a walk,
We are all alone.
The path goes on forever and ever, like space.
The trees are tall as skyscrapers and
I'm as small as a mouse.
The birds sing everywhere.
The further we walk in, the smell of smoke begins
And suddenly, a fire we see.
The crackle like guns frightens us a little.
I put my dog on her green lead and walk quickly by.
My brother threw some conifer on the fire
And *whoosh* the flames flew high.
We ran quickly to the safety of our home.

*Sam Bromage  (11)*
*Heathfield Community College*

# THE WOODS

When we went deep in the overgrown woods,
We could see nothing but green and brown.
This wood was an enormous wood.
The water on the leaves where it had been raining
Was running off and hitting my face with a thud.
The green blocked my view of anything.
How would I get home with the brown leaves
Grasping around my feet?
I could hear the cars in the background
And the odd bird calling loudly, but it was very quiet.
I felt like a man lost in a desert,
Scared whether I would get back or not.

*Ross Riley  (12)*
*Heathfield Community College*

## MY POEM

It was damp and dull one Monday afternoon.
The sky was like a palette full of grey paint.
Small spots of rain started dotting the ground,
I slowly started stumbling home in boredom.

In the distance I could hear the thunder rumbling,
Not even half way home and my tummy was grumbling.
The rain became heavy and quite fierce,
Stabbing into me like ice-cold needles.

Cars rushing past, through huge puddles splashing.
My legs were numb from the coldness of wet trousers,
Aching from walking up the steep slope.
Unable to jump, I plough through the huge puddles.

Home at last, wet and exhausted, but I'm home.

*Natalie Pyle  (12)*
*Heathfield Community College*


## MY POEM

We were in the unheated bed with chilled toes,
The moonlight shining through a crack in the curtain, like a torch.

Two cracks either side of the curtain
Where they had pulled themselves together
Looked like bats' wings.

Suddenly I heard a creak, I felt uneasy,
It sounded deadly, as if there was an intruder.
I hid under the covers, scared.

I did not want any part of my body to hang out.

*Daniel Bazen  (11)*
*Heathfield Community College*

# THE OLD THEME PARK

The wheels were hanging up in the night sky,
Rocking in the wind and rain,
The dodgems creaking under their own weight,
As though they were still in pain.

The bare roller coaster comes to a stop,
Towering over small stands,
The empty platform topped up with rubbish,
Deserted by the old band.

The ghost train stands in the dampened dark,
Hollow and empty as skulls,
The candyfloss stalls are full no longer,
The sweet smell attracted only by gulls.

*Alice Hampshire  (13)*
*Heathfield Community College*


# AUTUMN DAYS

The damp breeze lingers over the bare
And desolate hilltops,
While a thick blanket of mist is filling up
The valleys.
Leaves fall from towering giants and
Flutter lightly towards the ground.
The ground turns soft and muddy under a carpet
Of emerald and scarlet leaves.
Nights grow longer, with Christmas
Coming nearer,
Soon lakes will freeze and glisten
In the bleak autumn sunshine.

*Barnaby Alderson  (11)*
*Heathfield Community College*

# EMPTY THEATRE

Disused chairs bolted to the floor,
Ancient hinges creaking on the door,
Torn silk curtains lying on the stage,
Antique programmes missing their front page.
Creaking floorboards, hidden stairs,
Dingy wigs missing many hairs.
Cobwebs stuck in untouched corners,
The sound of many distressed mourners.
Music boxes playing in the past,
Old acting faces known as the cast,
Countless performances still to be performed,
The audience still yet to have yawned.
Costumes never to be worn,
This cannot be entered until dawn.

*Joe Richardson  (13)*
*Heathfield Community College*


# EVERYDAY HOLIDAY RECIPE

Take a few handfuls of family or friends,
Beat them into a queue for check-in,
Leave them to boil slowly for one hour,
Then whisk them through security onto the plane.
Leave them to settle for a good few hours,
Then scrape off plane into airport.
Place mixture in baggage collection
And allow to cool for ten minutes.
Tip out of airport into taxi and serve onto beach.
Leave to roast until golden brown.

*Paula Kells  (13)*
*Heathfield Community College*

## THE ABANDONED LIGHTHOUSE

The glistening white tower that stood proudly once,
Now stands forlorn, greening and flaking.
Crumbling mortar falls softly like rain, scattering dust,
Like talcum on the floor.
Echoes of past footsteps on the cold, glistening concrete
And corroded steel stairs.
Once shiny, reflective metal, now dull and tarnished
The first sprinkling of rust on the metal surfaces
Like autumn's first fallen leaves.
Glass once sparkling and clear, now opaque as
The eye of a dead beast, with creeping black mildew
Spreading dankly from the edges inward,
While dead flies decorate window sills.
The huge beacon now reduced to ashen greyness,
Moths that beat against it are dust.
Now, only the tower is lonely; the keeper long gone.

*Rowena Morris  (13)*
*Heathfield Community College*


## A BOOK IS

Everyday life,
A new beginning starting every single day,
It takes you to places that you've never been before,
You can forget about your worries,
Stepping into a new world, meeting new people, friends and family.
You can picture being someone else and have experience
Of what it's like living someone else's life.
You can be a fairy princess,
A mystery solver,
A heroine or a hero,
You could be evil, or you could be bad.

*Andrea Oakley  (14)*
*Heathfield Community College*

## THE EMPTY CASTLE

Entering, the musty air hit me like a wall
The deafening shriek of the door echoed in my ears,
The knight's armour creaked,
With the sharp-bladed axe.
I went down to the empty dungeon,
The castle had a sinister feeling.
A shivery breeze brushed past,
I heard the faint murmur of my name,
The desolate dungeon looked dismal.
Then a hollow figure appeared,
The air went dead,
The creaks and screams stopped
And then, it went with them,
To leave me in this castle as empty as space.

*Charlotte Lade (13)*
*Heathfield Community College*

## AUTUMN DAYS

Autumn days always amber,
Trees' leaves twirling to the morning dew,
Rain coming down side to side, pouring down like a drain,
Snow falling like a fluffy ball, but freezing cold,
Evergreen leaves never fall off,
When it rains you have to use an umbrella,
Usually you wear shorts and a T-shirt,
In November it always rains, especially on the 28th (my birthday),
Lovely, loveable warmth,
Months go by when Mexico is still hot, while England is still cold.

*Steven Songhurst (11)*
*Heathfield Community College*

## IF I WERE

If I were a natural disaster,
I would be a hurricane.
If I were a flying insect,
I would be a silky butterfly.
If I were a colour,
I would be purple.
If I were a gem,
I would be a sparkling emerald.
If I were an animal,
I would be a loveable cat.
If I were a flower,
I would be a pink and purple fuchsia.
If I were a part of the beach,
I would be the washy waves.
If I were a part of the night sky,
I would be a twinkling star.
If I were a planet,
I would be Venus.
If I were a book,
I would be a Point Horror.

*Aleha Backhouse  (12)*
*Heathfield Community College*


## CARNAGE

I crave for the taste of sweetness on my cornflakes,
So I creep downstairs and clamber upon the sideboard.
The sugar is nearly within my reach, I just need a hand hold,
And lo and behold, there is a cupboard to my right.

The airborne missile drives through the office block,
Like a paper plane into a house of cards.
An explosion like an earthquake and bomb rolled into one.
A national economy, literally up in flames.

People running wildly, with faces of blood and tears,
Innocent people dying on the spot.
To make it worse, the situation repeats itself,
Twice the damage, twice the terror.

I lean on the cupboard and hear the sound of breaking plaster.
The cupboard makes a sickening crash, not on the floor, on my heart.
The jars and packets all tumble down,
They smash on the floor like rocks from a skyscraper.

*David Evans  (13)*
*Heathfield Community College*


## THE MOON IS LIKE . . .

A touch,
A coin,
A lamp,
A wheel,
A shining light bulb,
A marshmallow,
A smiling teddy's face,
A round lump of salami,
A shiny sun,
The lid of a pen,
An iced bun,
A shiny piece of paper,
A ball of tin foil,
A mirror,
Silver ink,
The yolk of an egg,
A lump of potato,
A plate of beans,
A football.

*Sarah Puxty  (13)*
*Heathfield Community College*

## THE JOURNEY OF A STORM

The walk to Jane's house was a disaster.
The black clouds were appearing, faster and faster,
The rain was beating down, making me cold and wet,
This was the worst storm yet!
My umbrella was blown inside out,
The wind in my ear was as loud as a shout!
A roar of thunder shook the ground,
The sound was heard for miles around!
The lightning zigzagged across the sky,
'It's so scary,' I heard a boy cry.
When I reached Jane's front door,
The thunder gave a final *roar!*

The sun peeped out from behind a cloud,
'The storm must have finished!' Jane cried out loud.
We put on our wellies and a coat,
We brought out some paper and made a boat.
We put it in a puddle, which made it soggy,
But it was hours of fun for Jane's little moggy!
It was half-past five, time to go,
When up in the sky, I spotted a rainbow!

*Sarah Lias  (12)*
*Heathfield Community College*


## THE EMPTY FOOTBALL STADIUM

The ref blew the final whistle,
The disappointed fans flooded out of the ground.
After a few years, the pitch was replaced by thistles,
The desolate terraces were as empty as space.

A lone plastic bag flew in the wind,
The empty cups rattled as they fell down the steps,
The stench of old pies and mouldy tea filled the air,
The big screen stood tall, cracked and disused.

The tramps had moved into the tunnel,
The sign now read ''est 'am 'oot all 'lub,'
The crowds' chants still echoed round the ground,
The stadium sat there wondering if it would ever be used again.

*Tom Rothero  (13)*
*Heathfield Community College*

## MY AVERAGE DAY

I got home from school one day
And as I came into the house
I called to my mum
To let her know I was home.
I also shouted that I was going
Upstairs to my room
To do my homework.
After I had finished my homework,
I went downstairs and ate dinner.
While I was eating, I switched on the TV.
I watched the news, as it was on every single channel.
It read, 'Big News Flash - Terrorists Attack America'.
'What on earth are they talking about?' I wondered.

As I watched on, long into the night,
The true horror of the story unfolded.
Terrorism attacking America, by taking
Innocent lives away from those who owned them.
Also, those who lost friends and relatives,
Colleagues and just other people they knew,
Countless people could have lost their lives.
There are some feelings of relief when some
Are found alive, but not many.
That is my evening, perfectly normal for me,
But life-shattering for others.

*Adam Bridge  (13)*
*Heathfield Community College*

# I WAS ONCE . . .

I was once a baby, dribbling and so small,
I was once a toddler learning to crawl,
I was once a child playing with toys,
I was once a teenager interested in boys,
I was once a young woman leaving home,
The world is my oyster, I'm free to roam.
I was once a woman on her wedding day,
While the sun shines we shall make hay.
Before I knew it, I was a mother,
With hugs and kisses my baby I'd smother.
Now my two children are growing so fast,
Babies all seem a thing of the past.
Now we are alone again, my husband and I,
My husband suddenly becomes very ill and
We all wonder why, oh why?
My heart is broken, as is his,
Then follows the funeral, I weep and cry.
My life is cheered up again with grandchildren of my own,
It reminds me of my children, even though they're grown.
Now you see I'm old, my spoon I can hardly hold,
Now all that's left is a stone and writing typed in bold.

*Katie Chapman  (12)*
*Heathfield Community College*


# THE EMPTY ZOO

The misty moon shines down on the silent zoo,
Empty cages are crumbling away in time,
The rusty gate hangs off its creaky hinges,
Everything is still, not one sound can be heard.

A gentle breeze blows,
Whisking the rubbish around and around,
The dusty shops with shattered windows,
Broken park benches slowly rotting.

The pathways are littered with fallen leaves,
Overgrown ivy creeps up the decaying walls,
The deserted café is like a murky tomb,
The abandoned zoo is the shadow of death.

*Ellen English (13)*
*Heathfield Community College*


## MEMORIES

I got into bed, I had just been swimming and I was really tired.
I could hear the storm outside and knew that I wouldn't be
                                                able to sleep;
There were too many distractions. The leaves rustling,
The neighbours' dog howling like a wolf . . .

It circles the building like an eagle ready to grab its prey.
Faces of horror, shock and disbelief.
Men and women run from the falling giant-like building.
The faces of terror and fear from those in the building who know
There is no way out. They can either stay there and burn alive, or jump.

The thunder was so bad it was shaking the whole house.
The flashes of lightning through my blinds waking me every time
I managed to drift off. The shadow of the tree outside my window
Made me feel as if I was being watched as it swayed in the wind.

People appearing from buildings, shops, cars to see what
                                                was happening.
Emergency services flooding in from everywhere to try and
Help those few who had survived this massive blow.
The grey, depressing smoke rising higher and higher.
People in tears for any friends or family in what was once
One of the highest buildings in the world.
Few people appearing from the ruins of the massive building.

*Lara Brandt (13)*
*Heathfield Community College*

## THE WOODS

The sun shone brightly, like a giant lamp.
Trees blowing in the wind gracefully,
Leaves rustling as we walk.

Views forever as we walk fast,
Hills and dales for miles,
Grass tickling our skin as feathers do.

Birds bounce around in the sky,
Flying and screeching like monkeys
And we go on adventurously.

Animal noises in the distance,
Howling and swooping birds
Without any direction.

Now the end,
It is sad to leave the animals' home
In the woods.

*Nathan Hunt  (12)*
*Heathfield Community College*


## HOLIDAY

Take thousands of people at an airport,
Cram them into a craft,
Leave them to simmer for hours.
Stir well,
Take them out,
Leave them to cool down.
Cook them at 100c for a week,
Serve red hot!

*Graham Forster  (13)*
*Heathfield Community College*

## IN THE WOODS

Deep in the woods, under cover,
Surrounded by the bushes,
They're towering over me
So I can barely see the sky.

The holly bushes are prickly,
Yet I carry on regardless.
They are just a feature I accept is there.

All I can see are trees and bushes,
It is like a land of pure green,
I think it covers the whole Earth!

The only noise to be heard is a mild tinkling,
It is the sound of the waterfall,
As soft as a child's voice.

The place is a wild, daring adventure.

*Emily Hills  (12)*
*Heathfield Community College*


## THE CLOSED THEME PARK

I saw papers run on the ground,
I saw the ticket booth clicking round,
I heard the wind go round the rides,
I heard the whistling, I heard it glide,
I saw the sign swing with pride,
I saw the gate close behind,
I heard the rust grow on the rides,
I heard the mould grow on candy,
I left with a cold feeling of death.

*Rebecca Palmer  (13)*
*Heathfield Community College*

## MY GARDEN

Flowers dotted around the edge,
Trees engulfing the rear fence,
Like disintegrating pillars from an ancient villa.

The towering climbing frame,
The centre of my creativity,
With the solid bars for orbiting carelessly.

Around the final corner,
There is a mustard-yellow brick wall,
Like an obstacle that puzzles the mind endlessly.

A faint whistling of wind
That dodges in and out of the dark leaves,
Swirling around my hair
And through the splinter in the gate.

I feel delighted, as if my mother
Has just lifted me into the sky.

*Ellie Edmunds  (13)*
*Heathfield Community College*


## OUT OF THE CLASSROOM

Out of the classroom of the squeaking whiteboard,
Out of the classroom of the grumpy teacher,
Out of the classroom of the dog-eared books,
Out of the classroom of the flood of silence,
Out of the classroom of the cold, shivering mass,
Out of the classroom of the scribbled-on tables.

Into the corridor of the standing by the wall,
Into the corridor of the pushing and shoving,
Into the corridor of the budging out of the way,
Into the corridor of the pushing little people,
The crammed, full up corridors.

Into Mum's car of the warm, cosy seat,
Into Mum's car of the warm, rubber floor mat,
Into Mum's car of the cushioned head rest,
The funky radio in Mum's car.

*Emma Brockhurst (11)*
*Heathfield Community College*


## A JOURNEY

I closed the door and shouted goodbye
And looked up at the dark, cloudy sky.
I walked down my little road,
Jumping, to miss a passing toad.

I turned off the road to a narrow path,
Not hearing anything, not a cry, a sigh or even a laugh.
I kicked and scuffed at the brown and red leaves,
They were crumpled and wrinkled like my teacher, Mrs Reaves.

I walked through the fields full of bunnies and foxes,
I jumped over a stile clutching my lunch boxes.
Butterflies flew around in the air
And the blustery wind flew about in my hair.

I went onto the path that's small and narrow,
Oh, it's St Valentine's Day, you know Cupid with the bow and arrow.
I saw my friend and shouted, 'Hello,'
But he didn't hear me, he is as dippy as a dodo.

I started to run so I wouldn't be late,
As I ran, I caught up with my mate.
I managed as the bell went to just slip in,
Oh boy, oh great, now the lessons begin.

*Sarah Puttock (11)*
*Heathfield Community College*

## THE WOODS

A wondrous wood down in the valley,
About a mile away from my house,
It is tucked away from any hustle and bustle,
Just quiet, still, just living.

In this wood stands a gigantic conker tree.
Its long, leafy limbs stretch out above me.
Conkers fall like raindrops,
Flooding the carpet of the forest.

A blue sea of bluebells in the spring.
In the summer, the sun rays
Sparkle through the trees.
In the autumn, bracken turns to gold.

Twigs cracking, leaves crunching
Beneath my feet.
Birds twittering and squirrels chattering,
Pigeons cooing, the wind rustling in the trees.

Oh! This wonderful wood brings such joy to me.

*Samantha Smith  (13)*
*Heathfield Community College*


## IF I WAS . . .

If I was a colour, I would be the brightest blue.
If I was a chocolate, I would be the most expensive Belgian.
If I was a car, I would be sleek and streamlined.
If I was a volcano, I would be the most unpredictable.
If I was a precious gem, I would be a diamond worn by a star.
If I was a dress, I would be satin, slinky and shiny.
If I was a star, I would be the brightest of them all.
If I was a book, you wouldn't be able to put me down.

*Sarah Faulder  (12)*
*Heathfield Community College*

## THE TWO APPLE TREES

When I was small, I climbed into a big net,
Hung up by two apple trees, and the
Branches draped over me like wilted daffodils.

Between those two arms, I looked up at
The pale blue river, with little puffs of
Cotton wool floating down the stream.

While the wilderness surrounded me with
The sounds of the buzzing bumblebees
And the marching ants, I felt warm.

As I sit up, I gaze around at the
Hazy flowers, the aroma relaxes me
Into calm and relief.

I slowly drift away into peace.

*Emily Poile  (11)*
*Heathfield Community College*


## POEM

Warm, cuddly, soft and safe,
The best place I like to be.

Pretty and pink,
Flowery and bright,
Somewhere I am safe at night.

The wind, the rain, rattling at my window,
The clock, the TV,
I can hear them all,
It is nice for me.

I feel warm, sleepy and cosy.

*Daisy Cruttenden  (12)*
*Heathfield Community College*

# THE EYE

Out of the station, I'm finally here,
Out of the station with no souvenir,
Out of the station, the darkness has gone,
Out of the station, something is wrong,
Out of the station, I'm late for the Eye,
Out of the station, my friend's eating some pie.

Into the capsule, the time is now,
Into the capsule, it's all clear, wow!
Into the capsule, my mum's afraid,
Into the capsule, we've already paid,
Into the capsule, the wheel begins to creak,
Into the capsule, the clouds started to leak.

Into the sky it started to pour,
Into the sky, it's ten past four,
Into the sky, the Eye is tall,
Into the sky, the people are small,
Into the sky now nearing the end,
Into the sky, me and my friend.

*Matthew Digweed (11)*
*Heathfield Community College*

# THE EMPTY ZOO

The lights switched off, the great gates shut,
The animals alone, in ponds, caves and huts.
There were many tourists that came before,
Now there's just a guard sitting by the door.
All was silent besides a squawk or roar,
The shuffling of hooves and the lazy guard's snore.
The heavens split and it starts to rain,
Reptiles and mammals all going insane.
Silence shatters like a dropped glass.

The wind is swirling through the long, thick grass.
All take refuge away from the gale,
Yet they are soaked from head to tail.
Through the clouds comes a blink of light,
The rain has all gone, now it's all right.
Morning floods in like a raging sea,
Polar bears on ice, monkeys in a tree.
The proud lions out, the huge hippos too,
Everyone's ready for the opening of the zoo.

*Ian Burnett (13)*
*Heathfield Community College*


## IN MY HELICOPTER

I don't know where I'm going,
Across mountains, lakes and plains,
On an adventure I hope I go on again.

I see a city looming, with flashing lights.
Stars above and the city below,
Out of the city, back into the dark.

I carry on looking all around,
I start floating upwards,
Through the sky and up to the stars.

I keep on going, going, going,
I think I'm gone, but alas,
I land on a planet far away.

I meet another race,
In a land full of chocolate.
I live here now.

*Sophie Woollard (11)*
*Heathfield Community College*

## PRAGUE

Dark, misty mornings scattering the atmosphere,
A strange, mystical place named Prague.
What was in store for us?
No one knew.

Strange people, strange buildings, whole new world,
What would we do?
Large restaurants, the smell of Italian food drifted
Past my nose, my tummy rumbling.
What to do next?
No one knew!

Christmas dinner, carp,
Tender carp cooking, hungry, starving.
Iced-up lakes beginning to split as the
Clouds gradually vanished.
Stone roads, stone buildings, markets and crowds.

A strange world - Prague.

*Hannah Warmington (12)*
*Heathfield Community College*


## WAR RECIPE

Get two armies,
Add weapons,
Throw together,
Mix well, season with blood,
Leave to kill.
Add explosions and tanks,
Put flame-throwers in overkill for ten minutes,
Apply medics
And garnish with gangrene.

*Thomas Finch (14)*
*Heathfield Community College*

## SPONSORED WALK

We began our journey there and back,
First through the church,
Every child silent.

No turning back now,
Nearly there, nearly time to
Eat lunch in Vines Cross.

Everyone cheering, we were there,
We had our lunch, the grass was wet,
But we didn't care.

Up again to finish the walk,
Only a few miles to go.
I could see the end, a couple more steps
And we could be there.

*Sam Wickens  (12)*
*Heathfield Community College*


## CHRISTMAS

The Christmas tree stands tall, gleaming and glittering,
The lights on the tree twinkle, all bright,
The presents lay still under the tree
Awaiting their grand opening.

We sit down to a roast, smelling and feeling so sweet,
Adoring the crunchy potatoes,
We munch and crunch the crispy crackling,
Sucking on the meat soaked in gorgeous gravy.

We sit down and open the parcels of excitement.
Warm, cosy, joyful and cheerful,
Those are the feelings we have.

*Claire Barden  (12)*
*Heathfield Community College*

## APPLE CRUMBLE

Innocent bodies jumping out of windows
To face their pavement slab grave,
They would rather face the thousand foot drop
Than burn in the fuel of the plane.

Anger comes from every heart that beats,
Celebrations take place in Pakistan,
Photos of loved ones are pinned up in New York,
Who no one has seen or heard from.

Tears are shed, hugs hugged,
Television repeats footage of the crash,
Trade Centre comes down, smoke bellows out of the side,
More rescue workers lose their lives.

This plane of innocence pierced the heart of the World Trade Centre
And the hearts of New Yorkers also.
Programmes stopped, three minutes of silence
Were shared all across the world.

*Alicia Fordham  (13)*
*Heathfield Community College*


## THE BULLY

They walked up behind her,
Towering over her like a bird waiting to catch his prey,
Hitting and kicking her
Like some sort of toy.
Just something there to hit and tease.
The bully moves away and she runs in pain,
I watch as she cries,
She feels so lonely,
Worried they will come back.

She asks herself questions like,
'Why did they choose me?
Why am I different?'
I help her and sit with her,
But I just feel like a coward.
I didn't help her.
Why did I stand and watch?
All these questions that have no answers.

*Megan Welch  (11)*
*Heathfield Community College*


## THE FIRST DAY OF PLAYING

I'd always been looking forward
To seeing the big world,
But because I was so tiny,
I had to stay in.

Then the time came
To play in the big world.
When my mum let me out,
I was out and about.

I enjoyed myself in this world,
Except for the noisy cars,
Then after a while, I got to see my friends,
Because they lived up the road.

Soon it was time to come in
For my lovely, juicy dinner,
But I'd miss this part of the world
For playing outside in the sun.

This was the end of my day
And it was huge fun.

*Philip Head  (12)*
*Heathfield Community College*

# SPONSORED WALK

Off we set down the road,
The school going from sight,
Round church and steeple,
And other people,
Who were on a morning hike.

We went up steep hills and farm tracks,
The end of the group trailing back,
Then it was across the deep river,
The bridge wobbling made us quiver,
On we travelled, slowing each step.

We journeyed on, not long till lunch,
Sticks on the ground going crunch
As floods of people walked by,
Continually grumbling
As their tummies were rumbling.

Lunch gave us all a boost,
We no longer contemplated
A quick snooze.
Now, school in sight,
We zoomed home.

Aching muscles and stiff legs,
Plus a feeling we did get,
We'd done something well
And helped a bit,
Towards the school's art status bid.

*Peter Skelton (12)*
*Heathfield Community College*

# THE CONCERT HALL'S SECRETS

In the depth of the darkness,
When the hordes have returned,
A sudden blur from the background
Meant the day was adjourned.

The illusions that dwell there,
Not far do they stray,
They keep to the shelter
Till the closure of day.

It is right there and then
That the phantoms awaken,
They go to their merriment,
All hideouts forsaken.

The evacuated stage
Now host to the party
Of spectres, of wraiths
Innocuously hearty.

With a few hours to go
Till the tiers of seats fill,
The lemurs clean the area,
The routine midnight drill.

As rays of light creep
Upon the once vibrant scene,
Over three thousand people
Sit where the ghouls have once been.

*Jessie Stock  (13)*
*Heathfield Community College*

## SEPTEMBER 11TH

We're let free of our prison,
Katie and I laughing,
Struggling with homework,
Must get it done, but can't be bothered.
Talking, listening, giggling, remembering,
We turn on the radio . . .

The planes fly straight into the towers,
They don't care about the people inside,
The cries are deafening,
People run for their lives, not knowing what's happened.
Smoke engulfs everywhere,
Flame whip at the building, like a predator to its food.

Screams of horror are let out,
The buildings just crumble,
No one believes what they are seeing.
It can't be happening,
Where the towers stood is just empty.
On the floor are their remains,
The atmosphere around is dead . . .

Katie's mum calls,
Time to go home,
The end of another day,
Only to start all over again tomorrow,
The prison awaits our return.

*Emma Larkin  (13)*
*Heathfield Community College*

## ON HOLIDAY

We are all aboard the plane,
We're heading for sunny Spain.
The seats are rather cramped,
I thought, 'Have I packed my pants?'
Soon the food came round,
I don't think it'll stay down.
'Belt up,' said Dad,
Then I felt glad.

We are all at the hotel,
Which we know so well.
The same old smell
Which I knew well.
Next day we went to Aqua
With slides that feel like they're going to smack ya.
Other days we spent
With postcards to be sent.

Then we were off again,
Away from sunny Spain.
Another trip on the plane,
I was sitting next to a Dane.
Then we were near,
I was sucking a sweet to stop the popping in my ears.
An hour later and we were at home,
Mum was talking on the phone.
Next day we went to see Nan,
She said, 'My, you've got a tan.'

*Matthew Curd  (11)*
*Heathfield Community College*

## In My Garden

When I was little, about two or three,
I went into my garden, just me.
We had fun together, just Wig and me.

There were lots of wonderfully coloured plants,
There was a pink one, 'Very pretty,' said my aunts.
We went inside and my mum said, 'Do you want some tarts?'

I see a really amazing waterfall.
When the water runs down the sides,
It trickles into an admirable pool.
The clear water is very blue, but I can see some purple.

I can hear birds in the distance,
You can see them at a glance,
It reminds me of a chirpy dance.

This is cloud nine!

*Katie Fleat  (12)*
*Heathfield Community College*


## My Adventure Poem

We were small,
We went shopping,
I bought a toy dog and then
I flew on an aeroplane into the park.
It turned into a hot air balloon.
We were small and
Me and my friends ran home,
Very quickly, like a thunderbolt.

We were wearing white clothes
So the cars could see us.
Hello,
We are snowflakes dropping in the winter.
Winter is very hard,
Slippery floors,
Sliding children.
Winter's finished at last, snow has gone.

*Emily Jackson  (12)*
*Heathfield Community College*


# MY GARDEN

I gazed to the furthest corner of the garden,
I saw all the vibrant colours of flowers
That greet me every morning.

The grass, like a green carpet,
So lush and full of life,
A never-ending green road.

I look up and see the birds,
So cheerful and ecstatic,
Singing to a never-ending tune.

I hear the enormous trees overhead,
Rustle and sway to the wind,
The leaves falling like snowflakes.

My garden, so beautiful, so peaceful.

*Oliver Powell  (12)*
*Heathfield Community College*

## AUTUMN DAYS

Autumn approaches as summer departs,
Evening nights dim, misty breath in the air.
Leaves parachute to the dew-laden grass from
Twisted silhouettes of giant trees lit by the moonlight.
Daylight appears from the frosted hills
Giving hope and freshness to the wilting summer blooms.
The whistling wind blows huddled people,
Coats and scarves drawn tight.
Wizened branches bend and lose their final coat of
Leaves, naked to the world.
Busy squirrels gather acorns as they prepare for a
Cold, stark winter ahead, foraging through the vibrant colours
                                                of nature.
People and animals alike, alter their routine as winter is born.

*Simon Bond  (12)*
*Heathfield Community College*


## DEATH AND DUST

Crawling slowly through the packed corridors,
Desperately searching, I look left, I look right,
Nothing but crowds of people, the heat is intense.
All you can hear is the chaotic din of
Lots of people. Then I see it . . .

People were running everywhere like an army of hungry ants.
Everyone was terrified, the ground was shaking.
Then it happened. The towers fell. The whole world gasped.
The towers hit the ground, sending up a cloud of thick dust.
The dust was like a thick smog that engulfed everything.
Rescue teams arrived, they tried harder than anything,
But it was no good. The planes had done the damage.

*Craig Austen-White  (13)*
*Heathfield Community College*

## THE CLOSED CHURCH

The doors creak open like an ancient tomb
As I carefully step through, I see the gloom.
As I go a little further and brush a cobweb from my face,
I start to smell this musty, mouldy place.
I leave the doors open for a quick escape,
I don't know what I'll find, or how long it'll take.
The only light's the moonlight, shining through the door,
It illuminates the spiders that are creeping on the floor.
As I venture further, I feel someone watching me.
I turn around anxiously, but there's nothing to see.
Bells start ringing loudly, right in my ear,
I can sense a haunting feeling floating near.
I turn and run, I want to get out of sight,
Although I know someone is still watching me, on this misty,
                                                eerie night.

*Eloise Firrell  (13)*
*Heathfield Community College*


## AUTUMN DAYS

The days are rich red as the sun disappears.
The leaves fall to the floor forming a golden forest floor.
The trees are bare, but some trees stay green,
They are called evergreens.
The wind is biting like a razor.
Beautiful autumn days get shorter and shorter.
The wind whooshes around and around and around,
The ground is as white as a sheet.
The rain is splatting on the ground forming puddles,
Floating down to the ground, another golden leaf.
Lovely, golden, glittering ground as you walk around.

*Victoria Walter  (11)*
*Heathfield Community College*

# IF I WERE . . .

If I were a bird, I would be
An owl, soaring in the black, night sky.

If I were an instrument, I would be
A guitar, rocking every particle my music could touch.

If I were a cake, I would be
A soft strawberry delight with cream.

If I were a planet, I would
Shine and be seen more than a million miles away.

If I were an egg, I would
Be made of gold and covered with a thick layer of pearl.

If I were a book, I would be
Full of a great person's thoughts.

If I were a belt, I would
Break and humiliate a horrible man.

If I were a fruit, I would be
A melon, which when you eat the juice is so sweet
You can feel your mouth go numb.

*Kyle Fordham  (12)*
*Heathfield Community College*


# MY SPECIAL PLACE

We came to some old wooden gates that
Opened up to a quiet, smelly, cool place
With lots of bluebells everywhere.

The sparkling, special pond that shimmered
In the sun and warmed up, a great place
To go playing on the little island in the middle.

The big swing that sits two people,
With big, fat, strong, round ropes with twistable
Knots on both sides that hold the long, fat, wooden seat's weight.

The arch made from the trees and
The smell was of bluebells,
A lovely place to sit and relax.

You could fall asleep on a bent branch.

*Emily Wood  (11)*
*Heathfield Community College*


## THE CASTLE

Upon the grassy down it stood,
With towers six and a murky moat.
The sandstone walls in the midst of night,
Reminiscent of times long gone and lives forgot.

The great hall now exposed to the ink of night,
A carpet of grass and weeds concealing the tiles,
The turrets long collapsed, the walls crumbled,
Dissolved in siege and battles far off.

And wait! In the eerie darkness hear,
The clinking of armour, the blowing of flutes,
The cheering of crowds in the jousting arena.
And see! For a moment, while a star twinkles,
A maiden in a long, flowing gown,
With a gallant knight in a sparkling suit of armour.

We return to the present,
Where the castle is derelict, dire, dismal and plain.
Where the stars twinkle and the moon shines bright.
We depart from the scene, never to return,
But to never forget that enchanted, dark, green.

*Toby Farmiloe  (13)*
*Heathfield Community College*

## THE WORLD TRADE CENTRE

It feels like a pathway of no return,
Tranquil figures, wooden beams that burn,
Powdery ash covering the road,
Trucks are waiting for their load,
Sirens fading further away,
There's a cold chill, do I stay?
Tear-stained faces have been here before,
I can't stand this much more.
Flags and flowers are all around,
Who knows how many people have been found,
Dead or alive, heroes they are,
They're going up as a blazing star.
The emergency services will return when it's light,
But at the moment this will lie still for tonight.

*Charlotte Gower (13)*
*Heathfield Community College*


## JOURNEYS

Over the craggy hill,
Under the breaking bridge,
Through the round tunnel,
Around the steep green hill,
Between the two rocks,
Underneath the deep, blue sea,
Above the colourful reef,
Inside the dark cove,
Outside the cave the
Mermaids swim.

*Thomas Shand (13)*
*Heathfield Community College*

## THE TREE

I clambered the dirty steps
And when I got there,
My hands were all dirty.

When my brothers came,
They were a very unusual lot.
It began to get cold.

I descended to the ground,
Then it started to rain.

We were soaking wet.
When Mum came,
My brothers scrambled down.

I really like that big tree.

*Katie Berwick  (11)*
*Heathfield Community College*


## THE CLOSED LIGHTHOUSE

It was like a tall, striped football shirt;
Standing isolated, far out at sea.

The waves crashing against the rocks,
Like a cat and mouse at play.

Inside, a musty smell of dampened mould,
And steps upon steps to where?

Then came the answer of cracking glass
From the mighty broken bulb.

The sound of falling rocks and plaster;
And I leave it, desolated as ever.

*Hayley Alford  (13)*
*Heathfield Community College*

## THE ABANDONED STREET

Standing in the shadows of a lively, cheerful town,
Stood a lonely little street that lost its former crown.
People scurry past with their attention elsewhere,
Children sometimes go there, but only for a dare.
There used to be a market, every other day,
But after the Great Fire, most people stayed away,
For you see, many years ago a tragedy occurred,
Something so very terrible that all the country heard.
On a sultry summer night when most people where asleep,
A naughty child left his bed and stepped out in a creep.
With a flick of his wrist, he lit a match and threw it to the ground,
Making sure no one could see, he ran without a sound.
Some passers by spotted the flames and dialled 999,
The operator comforted them by saying everything would be fine.
Only five people could get out and escape the fire,
Days on, when going through the rubble the death toll rose higher.
An elegant, modern shopping centre was built right next door,
And so the sombre street will stand, forgotten evermore.

*Emily Skelton  (13)*
*Heathfield Community College*

## IF I WAS A . . .

If I was chocolate, I would be a milky-white Galaxy
Smothered in sprinkles.
If I was a car, I would be a blood-red, flashy Ferrari
With a black, pull-back hood.
If I was a picture, I would be a swirling whirlpool of colours.
If I was the weather, I would be a smiling, welcoming, golden sun.
If I was a building, I would be a gigantic skyscraper with eighty floors.

If I was a Sunday lunch, I would be a steaming hot, roast chicken
with roast potatoes.
If I was a country, I would be a proud, large, perfect country.
If I was a day, I would be Christmas, snowy, white and welcoming.
If I was a clock, I would tick happily on my wall, being useful.
If I was a poster, I would show anything in the world.

*Alex Wells  (12)*
*Heathfield Community College*


## THE CLOSED PRISON

The echoing of the rattling ball and chains,
The dampness and coldness of the dark, scary cells,
The outrageous noise of the old prison bells,
The black and white uniforms, done and dusted,
The stench of the mouldy cells where criminals were busted.
The sound of the prisoners while lifting weights,
Watching security guards, guarding the gates.
The closed, dusty book, where you will see names,
The empty hall, where they liked to play games.
The offices, still posh and clean,
The dining room where cooks are mean.
The open playing field where prisoners played,
The big brown doors, where from there it's the big, bad courts.
The tiny Alsatians with the personality of a beast,
The happy times at Christmas, where everyone feasts.
The rusty cell bars keep prisoners in at night,
The coppers who always break up the fights,
The disgusting stew is always cooked in a pot.
When there was noise, now nothing.
Silence is all I've got.

*Michael Berwick  (13)*
*Heathfield Community College*

## MY SPECIAL PLACE

As I entered this cold, dusty room,
Something lit up inside me
And something made me stare.

It was an object that I remembered,
Sitting in the corner, its face was brown
With a little pink nose.

It was my old teddy bear,
It was sitting staring at me with
Its beady eyes and web-infested body.

Then I began to look around
And everything became much clearer.

I saw books stacked on the shelf
And toys scattered over the floor.

I was in my bedroom.

*Mia Archer  (11)*
*Heathfield Community College*


## IF I WERE . . .

If I were a food, I would be a bright, orange carrot.
If I were an instrument, I would be a keyboard with lots of tunes.
If I were an animal, I would be a Bengal tiger.
If I were a dinosaur, I would be a huge brachiosaurus.
If I were a sweet, I would be a creamy Cadbury's chocolate.
If I were a bird, I would be a small, white owl.
If I were material, I would be a blue, fluffy type.
If I were a soft drink, I would be a sharp lemonade.
If I were a sound, I would be a tinkling chime.

*Charlotte Wickens  (12)*
*Heathfield Community College*

## INTO DOG TRAINING

Out of the car, I have arrived,
Out of the car, will I survive?
Out of the car, people stare,
Out of the car, here I come, beware,
Out of the car, I approach the hall,
Out of the car with my dog's ball.

Into the hall I will go,
Into the hall, best behaviour on show,
Into the hall, with treats in my hand,
Into the hall, the naughty corner is where I stand,
Into the hall, I go to train,
Into the hall, but my dog is a pain.

Into dog training, I try to be cool,
Into dog training, I look a fool,
Into dog training, the teacher is there,
Into dog training, and her dog with grey hair,
Into dog training, a test to pass,
Into dog training, again I'm last.

*Craig Chapman  (11)*
*Heathfield Community College*


## THE JOURNEY INTO SLEEPY-SNOOZY LAND

As I closed my eyes and thought of sleep,
I tried in vain to count my sheep.
They leaped and gambolled to and fro,
Slow down sheep, where do you go?
'To the man in the moon and far away,
We keep on running till the break of day.'
As I closed my eyes and thought of sleep,
I dreamed . . .

*Aidan Lee  (11)*
*Heathfield Community College*

## OUT OF BED

Out of bed, from the warmth,
Out of bed, leave my teddy behind,
Out of bed, ready to get dressed,
Out of bed to the sound of my alarm,
Out of bed into colder air,
Out of bed, go downstairs.

Into the bus, from the rain,
Into the bus, I'm dry again,
Into the bus to chat with my friends,
Into the bus, I look at my watch,
Into the bus, it's ten past eight,
Into the bus, we're going to be late.

Into school and rushing down the corridor,
Into school to registration,
Into school, so many people it's like a station,
Into school and up the stairs,
Into school and the bell rings for hometime,
Out of school and on the bus,
Everyone makes hometime such a fuss.

*Aimé Grzesik (12)*
*Heathfield Community College*


## LATE AUTUMN

Whoosh! The sudden gust of wind blasting
Against the defenceless windows of a house.
Smash! The hailstones bashing against
The door, like rounds of a powerful rifle.

Crash! An ancient oak tree flattens
Everything in its path as it crashes to
The ground from a hundred feet in the air.

Shriek! A terrified old lady is blown
Into the sky by an awesome gale of about 70mph,
With her umbrella open over her head,
Protecting her from the torrential rain.

Hooray! The people cheer, for very soon
Winter will be here, the fluffy snow,
Snowball fights and snowmen.
But the people here still gravely fear
The autumn, for they fear it is a bad omen.

*Liam Reilly (11)*
*Heathfield Community College*


## THE POWER CUT

Out of power, everything's black,
Out of power, will it ever come back?
Out of power, my brother's getting worried,
Out of power, 'Come on Mum, hurry!'
Out of power, how long will it take?
Out of power, what a mess we could make!

Into darkness, it feels like the night,
Into darkness, the dog's out of sight,
Into darkness, Mum's come home,
Into darkness, we're no longer alone,
Into darkness, night's nearly here,
Into darkness, when will light reappear?

Into light, it's come back now,
Into light, how it left, I don't know how,
Into light, not scared anymore,
Into light at around half-past four,
Into light, the electric key's got ten,
Into light, I hope it won't happen again.

*Hollie Trinder (11)*
*Heathfield Community College*

## AUTUMN IS LOVELY

A utumn turns the world amber,
U mbrellas lifted against the rain and harsh winds,
T rying to break from their master's grip,
U nder tall and towering trees, people shelter from the rain,
M onths of autumn keep us happy,
N ights and nights of lovely autumn.

I n beautiful starlight, people look out of their windows at the stars.
S tars in autumn look even nicer than in any other season.

L uscious leaves glisten on the swinging branches of the trees,
O h autumn, you're the best season of them all,
V iolet flowers are scarce and few,
E vergreen trees stand proud and tall with all their leaves,
L ovely autumn, stay with us please,
Y ou're fading away, don't go please!

*Jennifer Cook  (11)*
*Heathfield Community College*


## AUTUMN POEM

Autumn, autumn, autumn,
It's the best season we have.
I love sitting in my nan's conservatory
Listening to the rain pitter-patter on the clear roof.
When I go to the park, there's dew on the grass,
Mist in the air.
I can see lots of things that make me stare.
I love autumn and I hope it never ends.
Because I love autumn so much,
I will be sad when it passes.

*Charlotte Hedley  (11)*
*Heathfield Community College*

## AUTUMN IS HERE

A mber trees are all around in autumn,
U mbrellas usually unfold against unwanted rain,
T oadstools try to tackle treacherous weather and grow,
U nseen wind undertakes stealing umbrellas in an updraft,
M onths of autumn make morning dew which means messy mud,
N uns in November nick Nicky's nuts, so naughty Nicky nicks nuts
from nauseous nurses.

I ce is important in ponds and ice injures interesting fish,
S uddenly unsuspecting trees' leaves seem to drop.

H allowe'en has come, so happy hordes dressed as hairy hags harass
householders for Haribo sweets!
E very elephant evidently escapes the fact it's autumn at all!
R oaring rockets remind us of rebels.
E very autumn ends eventually and even though autumn shall come
again soon, everyone will miss it come winter.

*Alun Williams  (12)*
*Heathfield Community College*


## AUTUMN DAYS

Leaves falling, are as red as blood.
When snow falls, it's like a massive flood!
Outside it's really too cold to bear,
It's so cold, it's freezing my hair!
To go outside and play with the leaves,
I look up and see the leafless trees.
Friends stay in to keep nice and warm,
The fire's roaring like a massive storm.
Christmas is coming, it's really near,
I can't believe it's almost here!

*Bryony Mason  (11)*
*Heathfield Community College*

## THE WOOLLY JUMPER

Off the sheep, grazing in the field,
Off the sheep, following his brothers and sisters,
Off the sheep, farmer's watching him closely,
Off the sheep, wool like a cloud,
Off the sheep, looking lonely,
Off the sheep, bleating out loud.

To the factory and loud machines,
To the factory, people being noisy and shouting,
To the factory, boxes piled up high,
To the factory, machines working away,
To the factory, dark grey colours,
To the factory, people working hard.

To the shop with other jumpers,
To the shop, bright green and red stripes,
To the shop, packed into boxes,
To the shop, put out on display,
To the shop, other colours around,
To the shop, waiting to be found.

*Alice Wettle  (11)*
*Heathfield Community College*


## AUTUMN TIME IS HERE

Drip, drip, drip, the autumn rain starts to pour.
A bright and colourful day has started with rain.
Trees lose their leaves and they flutter to the ground,
Red, orange, yellow and green.
The loveliest autumn colours I've ever seen.

The rain stops, the birds sing for the
Start of an autumn morning.
Squirrels get ready to sleep until spring,
The mists meander through the meadows and
Frost covers everything in sight, there's no more summer light.

Fires burn in cosy, country houses,
Time flies as the effect is shown.
Trees look dead, everywhere is cold and wet.
Autumn is here.
This happens every year.

*Corrine Redfern  (12)*
*Heathfield Community College*


## DEAD ANGELS

Into the roar of the unfeeling sea,
The clang of the bell, lost to the waves,
On crumbling white cliff, shrouded in mist,
The long-deserted lighthouse stands.

The frigid wind whips salted railings,
The whitewashed walls, grey with age,
Once tended and cared for by lonely men,
So long dead, their memories fade.

Light that showed sanctuary to so many vessels,
The guardian angel to ships in the cove,
Now he's useless, shattered and cold,
Scattered across the lighthouse floor.

This sceptre of light, protection from night,
Its ancient circle now complete,
Its crumbling foundation washed out to sea,
Floating on a distant shore.

The sand on this beach, harvested now
For building work beside the quay,
This sand, as old as Earth itself,
Is sentry for the land once more.

*Zara Preston  (13)*
*Heathfield Community College*

## AUTUMN

A utumn leaves, crisp and brown
   fall off the trees and come tumbling down.
U nderneath the yew tree sit tall and proud,
   waving like giants all around.
T urn all around and you will see
   squirrels gathering nuts for their tea.
U sual rain comes plummeting down,
   falling, tumbling, around and around.
M any spectacular sounds and smells,
   the howling wind and the bonfires burning.
N ow comes the time, November is near,
   the autumn nights draw nearer, nearer, and then
   the warm autumn is gone.

*Lea Bradford  (11)*
*Heathfield Community College*


## GOLDEN TREES

G listening, golden, glowing, green, tall trees.
O ctober is the time for orange leaves falling down,
L ovely leaves whistle through the wind,
D ying leaves falling into a pile,
E ager winter coming,
N earer.

T umbling, terrible trees cracking in the wind,
R aging rivers swirling around,
E merald, soft, dewy grass,
E very night closes in,
S hining snake slithered along the slippery grass.

*Charlotte Mott  (11)*
*Heathfield Community College*

## AUTUMN COMES!

Autumn comes . . .
Blood-red roses spring out of their buds,
Golden leaves lay lazing like a forest bed,
Treacherous trees towering in silhouettes,
Whistling winds winding all over.
Autumn comes.
Luscious colours appear as sweet as heaven itself,
The morning dew on the grass, a bed of colour,
A downpour beating against our faces,
Falling, floating, flowing.
Autumn comes.
It's so astonishing and wonderful, a good place to be,
So, so long summer, here is autumn,
A lovely season.
I'll be sad to see it go.

*Siobhan Givan  (11)*
*Heathfield Community College*


## AUTUMN DAYS

A   utumn is here today,
U   sually comes before winter,
T   rees are brown,
U   p above us,
M   onths September and October are in autumn,
N   ovember is the end.

D   ecides that Christmas should come,
A   fter all the excitement,
Y   et winter needs to come.
S   easons are great, aren't they?

*Kimberley Musson  (11)*
*Heathfield Community College*

## My Gran's Garage

We would sit,
In the dark and damp place,
Of my gran's garage.

The noise of the drains
Would be the army clattering into battle.
Under the car would be the muddy, swamp forest.

We would play camps,
Or play with soldiers,
And use ketchup as blood.

Empty biscuit tins would be the army base.
The creaky door would cry, 'armies out.'
My gran's garage as a battlefield!

My gran's dark and gloomy garage as a battlefield.

*Miles Hoimans  (11)*
*Heathfield Community College*


## It's Autumn Now

Golden leaves falling slowly,
Autumn is here and I am lonely.
No one's here to play with conkers,
I think they must be bonkers.
Carpet of leaves
And leafless trees,
Coming over are my friends,
Sometimes they drive me round the bend.
Snow is coming
And in the snow, I'll be running.

*Zoe Curtis  (11)*
*Heathfield Community College*

## My Garden?

As I gaze towards the sparkling grass,
Happy thoughts of my past come into my mind.
The soft, warm grass under my feet.

As the grass slips through my slippery toes,
Fresh, clean air filling my lungs,
Playing in my garden all around my sand.

Filling up my buckets, a sandcastle so tall,
As my fingers let all the sand to my feet,
So big, my castle stands all around.

Splash, splash, the rain starts to fall,
As I run for the shelter of a warm, safe home,
I look out of the window.

I see my garden?

*Danielle Cumberworth  (12)*
*Heathfield Community College*


## The Empty Lighthouse

In the midst of the moonless sky,
The daunting tower stood high.
The sinister structure, crumbled and rusty,
Inside so eerie, chilling and musty.
The ancient twisted staircase seemed to go on forever,
Whilst the colliding waves crashed together.
The dim beam shone around an isolated bay,
Like a cloudy night sky in May.
Through cracked windowpanes came whistling wind,
Like a ghost's whisper echoing.
The booming thunder shook the walls,
But the storm will be over when daylight calls.

*Sam Sherwood  (13)*
*Heathfield Community College*

## SPONSORED WALK

On a summer's morning just after nine,
My friends and I linked arms in a straight line,
The birds were singing,
My ears were ringing,
As we set off, the sun began to shine.

Down quiet country lanes a few cars pass by,
My stomach rumbles for an apple pie.
Chatter fills the air,
We play 'Truth or Dare.'
As the time passes quickly, we all sigh.

Across grassy fields, over wooden styles,
We see a church and a house with red tiles.
Hills merge far away,
What a lovely day
As we finish our walk, over six long miles.

*Hazel Levy (12)*
*Heathfield Community College*


## SCHOOL RECIPE POEM

Take a thousand or so pupils and put them in a school,
Add a few teachers for flavour and sprinkle with books and pens.
Leave to work for a few hours and allow time for them to settle.
Throw some food in and whip into a frenzy.
Allow the mixture to settle again.
Turn up heating, leave to stew in a cramped room for one hour.
Finally, transfer into several buses and allow it to cool in
different houses.
Serve with computers and playgrounds.

*Daniel Morgan (13)*
*Heathfield Community College*

## MY BEDROOM

When I was fed up,
I went into my room,
Just looking around at the yellow walls,
Which were as bright as the sun.

Thought to myself, how boring
It was just looking around,
So I quietly and slowly with no noise,
Got out something and placed it on my pink bed.

Got out the grey pain and splash!
I became small hoping no one would see me,
I was in trouble in red letters
And a capital 'T'.

I walked away smelling the smell of air freshener,
Off I went, so small and not wanting to know
A single thing about it.
I was invisible and staying that way.

*Katherine Reilly (11)*
*Heathfield Community College*

## IF I WAS . . .

If I was a pie, I would be a succulent pork pie.
If I was a chocolate bar, I would be a chunky Yorkie.
If I was a sandwich, I would be peanut butter and jam on
                                                    tasty, white bread.
If I was a tree, I would be a giant redwood.
If I was a vegetable, I would be a crunchy orange carrot.
If I was a car, I would be a bright yellow Porsche.
If I was a flower, I would be a sleepy sunflower.
If I was an animal, I would be a large, lazy lion.

*Zak Pooley (12)*
*Heathfield Community College*

## THE BRIDGE

A hidden place
With creaky boards,
Sheltering nesting trees,
And leaves like paper crunching.

The water glistens in the sunlight,
With twigs bobbing down the stream.
Down I go and swing across the water,
Hopping from stone to stone.

The wind whistles, the birds flap
And the trees sway and rush.
What an exciting place to be,
And there's so much to do and see.

*Claudia Thomas  (11)*
*Heathfield Community College*


## AUTUMN

Winter is a time for sadness,
'Cause summer has just gone,
But maybe there is time for joy,
As Christmas is yet to come.

The colours of the autumn months
Are like nothing you will see.
Red, amber, yellow and brown
Are found on a simple tree.

Autumn finishes very fast,
There's nothing you can do,
So just wait for one year,
It will happen very soon.

*Nicky Ellis  (11)*
*Heathfield Community College*

## THE FOREST ROCKS

In the quiet forest, there stood the rocks,
The peaceful, dark rocks which I loved.
They stood frozen in the forest, just like statues.

The rocks piled on top of each other,
Just like a tall stack of books,
Books piled high and unevenly on a shelf.

Looking as if they were about to tumble,
But as strong as a four hundred-year-old tree.
They stood like a lion, standing tall,

A lion who has battled to become king,
King of the jungle
And ruler of the world.

The rocks: my favourite place to be.

*David Randall (11)*
*Heathfield Community College*


## ROOM OF SILENCE

As I walk into my bedroom,
It's as bright as a painting shining in the sun,
The smell of sweet sugar candy sticks fills the air.

As I settle down on my bed, it's secret,
Warm and cosy, where there is no noise,
But the wind rushing in and out of the leaves.

How my sister and I fight in my room,
But then my sister starts crying,
I feel guilty for what I have done.

A silence falls in my room.

*Kirstie Leeves (11)*
*Heathfield Community College*

# THE FIELD

The crunching noise of the
Frost was drowned out
By the cold, bitter wind.

The vast desert of snow
On the field, diamond snowflakes,
Sparkled with the rising sun of morning.

My darting dogs were blurs
Of light, printing their paws in the snow,
While snowballs flew between us.

The freezing goalposts smudged
With the background as a beautiful landscape
Painted by the artist of winter.

*Anthony Matsell  (11)*
*Heathfield Community College*


# THE THEME PARK AFTER CLOSING TIME

As the turnstiles click their last farewell,
And the children's laughter disappears,
The Twister settles to its place of rest
And the ghost train sits in sinister quiet.

The fast-food shutters drop like hail,
Only the wind visits deserted tables.
Some rubbish takes flight like a kite at the beach
And the circus tent covers emptiness.

The beam of the night watchman's torch spears the dark
And catches the sleeping roller coaster.
The metal chains echo around the rides.

*Victoria Fletcher  (13)*
*Heathfield Community College*

## THE OLD HOUSE

When I walk through the door,
It hits me with flying colours
Of the days that used to be.

Like a child anxious to find out,
I run and run, but I don't get anywhere.
I reach the door, it opens,

I look out into the hall, not as excited.
There they are, my sisters, crying,
Like the world was about to end.

I was turned around and told the news
And I lost my heart when I heard the words,
'Death . . . Dad . . .'

And that's when I realised the world had ended.

*Rebecca Vine  (11)*
*Heathfield Community College*


## THE GREAT, BEAUTIFUL AMAZON

The great, beautiful Amazon, the size of Western Europe,
It's a place where they adore their syrup,
The evil farmers cut down the trees,
The natives have nowhere to be.
The strange and ugly natives have a song for you and me,
'Humble, bumble, tumble, sumble, dumble, dee,'
which means, 'We poor people are dying.'
You are probably sighing.
If we've warned them once,
Then we've warned those farmers a dozen times.

*Callum Kirk  (11)*
*Heathfield Community College*

# THE RUINS OF THE PRISON

Through the locked doors and bolted gates,
Across the grass, the empty prison stands.
The bricks crumble, the walls waste,
Metal rusts and paint flakes away.

Inside the walls the place is like
An empty cave in the middle of a desert.
It's desolate and creepy
And sends chills down your spine.

You can hear dead men's voices
Chattering and laughing in the air.
The cramped cells still look inhabited with sheets, pillows,
Plates and cutlery littered around.

The clinking of keys echoes around
And the clanking of doors shakes the floor.
The squeaking of hinges, eerie and shrill,
Makes the empty space even more mysterious.

Years later the aged prison is gone
And now in its place,
A brand new housing estate stands,
But beneath the bricks, the old convicts lay in wait.

*Tristan Shortland  (13)*
*Heathfield Community College*


## PICTURE ME

If I were a board game, I would be draughts or chess,
If I were a sports brand, I would be Ellesse,
If I were a car, I would be a racing Ferrari,
If I were a meal, I'd be rich in vitamin C,
If I were a country, I would be great Hungary.

If I were a flower, I would be a dainty lily,
If I were a jigsaw, I would have 10,000 tiny pieces,
If I were a mountain, I would be amazing Everest,
If I were a rock, I would be very hard and black,
If I were a tree, I'd be an oak tree standing tall.

*Catherine Miller  (13)*
*Heathfield Community College*


## JOURNEY IN THE PAST

I ride looking for a new life.
The country air is blowing around my face,
I feel free, I have no worries,
My mind just thinks of what's ahead.

I travel on, I see a farm,
Smelling healthy and alive.
Cows are being milked,
Horses are being ridden.

I venture on with my journey,
I come across a stream crystal clear,
Lily pads glide peacefully along,
I carry on riding with all ahead of me.

Finally I reach my destination,
The comfort of a small village.
A small farm for sale,
Buy it I shall do.

I now look back twenty years later,
I'm living on my farm as happy as can be.
I think to myself how worthwhile my journey was
And I just can't help myself smiling.

*Matthew Payne  (11)*
*Heathfield Community College*

## THE CLOSED FACTORY

As dark as a coffin at night,
The closed factory stands
Dark, ample and echoing.
The steel pillars and beams creak,
Abandoned machines, old cardboard boxes,
The boss's swivel chair,
Closed for twenty years,
Soon to be demolished, the factory will be no more.
The workers' spirits live here,
Many of them perished in the fire of '81.
Now a home for all sorts of creatures,
Crumbly brickwork falling to the ground,
Now all that's left is a smelly, mouldy place.

*Matthew Roberts  (13)*
*Heathfield Community College*


## DARK PLAYGROUND

All dark and grey,
The play park stands.
No one goes there anymore.
The smell of rotten wood hangs in the air.
Old and greying,
The wooden climbing frame creaks in the wind.
Splintered and rusty,
The swings hang loose.
It casts shadows,
Like a giant looming over the playing field.
The play park stands alone.

*Martin Scott  (13)*
*Heathfield Community College*

## THE EMPTY SCHOOL

As I entered through the long shattered door,
I felt an icy draught as I stepped on the floor.
It took a while to carry on as I was frozen now,
I slowly unfroze and wiped the sweat from my brow.
The deserted barracks of education and life,
This piece of architecture looks like it's lived all its life.
Long gone were the days when children swarmed here,
It now lays quite tranquil, not one juvenile near.
Old marked papers carpet the floor,
As a symbol of the labour of teachers before.
As I go on through halls, haunted by ghosts of boffins,
And now their long dead bodies asleep in their coffins.
The walls absorbed sloth and lie slack in the rooms,
At the front of the classroom a web-tapestry looms.
A fresco of hardened dust adorns the ceiling,
And I'm possessed by this cold, tingling feeling.
I can't stay much longer, my memories are in my mind,
And I've seen enough, I'll leave the past behind.

*Ben Evans  (13)*
*Heathfield Community College*


## IF I WAS A . . .

If I was an item of stationery, I would be a long red and blue rubber.
If I was a colour, I would be a deep metallic green.
If I was a country, I would be one of the sunny Canary Islands.
If I was a sport, I would be professional football.
If I was a disaster, I would be a bright, sparkly volcano.
If I was a musical instrument, I would be some shiny drums.
If I was a sandwich, I would be a scrumptious chicken and tomato
ketchup on white bread.

*Dani Ford  (12)*
*Heathfield Community College*

# MY RABBIT

Bumble is my rabbit,
She has a painful habit,
She scratches you with her claws,
But she has very soft paws.
She eats all day,
Has nothing to say,
She is black and round,
Makes no sound.
Bumble loves to eat grass,
She can run extremely fast.
She nibbles her hay
Every single day.
Her whiskers twitch,
She likes to itch.
She can jump very high,
She loves to sleep and lie.
Her fur's all fluffy,
Her tail's very puffy,
That's my rabbit, Bumble.

*Emily Malins  (11)*
*Heathfield Community College*


# ROMANTIC POEM

I see him from afar, sitting,
A dark shadow in a corner.
Lights glitter off his eyes,
Like a moon dancing on a river.

I'm happy from the glowing moon,
Stars are shining which remind me of his eyes.
I can't describe how I feel inside,
All I know is I don't want it to go.

If only I could tell him how I feel,
There is still a feeling that stops me.
He needs to know, but I can't say,
It's just going to have to stay
A secret of mine.

*Linda Mileman  (11)*
*Heathfield Community College*


## MY OPERATION

Scratchy new pyjamas,
Cosy new slippers,
Nurses' rustling uniforms,
Lights dim,
When can I go home?
Whispering voices,
Nil by mouth,
Bright lights overhead,
Green facemasks,
Counting to ten,
Hot face,
When can I go home?
Dry mouth,
Never-ending nights,
Crying, coughing, calling,
When can I go home?
I look at the window,
Wind blowing
Cool air,
Running, playing, laughing,
Fruit bowl,
Cards and chocolate,
When can I go home?

*Charles McKie  (11)*
*Heathfield Community College*

## MY BEDROOM

Climbing the mountain
Across the desert
To my pillow.

Jumping in piles of snow
As soft as clouds
In my clothes.

Building walls of bricks
Up to the stars and beyond
With my toys.

Reading pages of words
Big and small
From my books,

And this was me when I was small.

*Magnus White  (11)*
*Heathfield Community College*


## IF I WAS . . .

If I was a flower, I would be a tall, grand tulip.
If I was the weather, I would be sunny as it makes everyone happy.
If I was a fruit, I would be a sweet strawberry.
If I was a colour, I would be calm, refreshing lilac.
If I was a chocolate bar, I would be a fun-filled Double Decker.
If I was a book, I would be 'Harry Potter and the Goblet of Fire,'
As it is fun-packed and full of adventures.
If I was a musical instrument, I would be a graceful flute.
If I was a precious gem, I would be a gleaming diamond.

*Emma Hale  (12)*
*Heathfield Community College*

## The Special Garden

As I entered the warm, shadowy garden,
It smelt like newly-cut grass.
As I sat down, the sun shone on the back of my head.

When I was sitting down,
The rabbit came and hopped onto my lap,
With a daffodil in its mouth.

As I looked up to the blue
Cloudy sky, there were seagulls
Flying through the air.

I got up to look at the
Colourful flowers that
Were planted in the flowerbed.

The flowers were as tall as the garden fence.

*Calvin Foster  (12)*
*Heathfield Community College*


## Picture Me As . . .

If I was a book, I'd be an adventurous Harry Potter book,
If I was a planet, I'd be fiery Venus,
If I was an animal, I'd be a roaring tiger,
If I was a theme park ride, I'd be a looping roller coaster,
If I was a day of the week, I'd be fun and friendly Friday,
If I was a star, I'd be the shiny North Star,
If I was a mythical creature, I'd be a fire-breathing dragon,
If I was a country, I'd be mountainous, snow-peaked Sweden,
If I was a colour, I'd be bright orange.

*Emily Dudley  (13)*
*Heathfield Community College*

## THE TREE

When I climb the twisted bark,
Leaves are like decorations on a Christmas tree.
From high above you can see the Earth turning, twisting around the sun.

Raindrops fall from the grey blankets above and a waterfall will appear,
There are curves as if rocks are stuck to the leaves.
The ancient tree seems so wise, knowing secrets of everything in sight.

It stands so firm and proud, overlooking smaller trees and fields,
The sun reaches out at midday and grasps the dangling greens tightly,
The drooping branches reach the ground and can be wrapped around
                                                        the world.

When the wind comes, it blows a tune and
Then the leaves and branches start to dance.
The giant tree, it reaches the misty clouds drifting past.

The tree will live on without revealing its secrets to the world.

*Petro Turton  (11)*
*Heathfield Community College*


## IF I WAS . . .

If I was a book, I would be easy to read,
If I was an animal, I would be a shy but cheeky monkey,
If I was a sandwich, I would be a smelly cheese and onion,
If I was a fruit, I would be a big, fat apple,
If I was a CD, I would be Dido's 'No Angel,'
If I was a TV programme, I would be a soap,
If I was a PlayStation game, I would be 'Time Slip,'
If I was an insect, I would be not a daddy-long-legs, but
                                        a Lucy-long-legs.

*Lucy Saunders  (12)*
*Heathfield Community College*

## THE TREE HOUSE CHILDREN

When we climbed the rickety ladder of the tree house,
We were eye level with the rooftops
Of the neighbouring houses and their smoking chimneys.

Like spiky holly leaves they pierced the sky,
Red, plump berries clustered between them
And they grew under a blanket of clouds.

We were big and thought we knew everything
Worth knowing in our strong, sturdy
Tree house that had seen so much change.

What a view from its branches.
In every direction we can see the far-off
Downs, the sea, the towns.

We could fly on the wind.

*Debbie Vince  (11)*
*Heathfield Community College*


## IF I WAS A . . .

If I was a colour, I'd be calm, glistening blue,
If I was a song, I'd be the quiet song of 'Angels,'
If I was weather, I'd be blankets of beautiful, crisp, cold snow,
If I was a book, I'd be the imaginative Harry Potter series,
If I was an instrument, I'd be a softly flowing flute,
If I was a sweet, I'd be a crunchy, velvet Malteser,
If I was a planet, I'd be bold Saturn,
If I was an item of clothing, I'd be a warm, snuggly jumper.

*Sophie Atkinson  (12)*
*Heathfield Community College*

## THE BEDROOM

The small, dull room,
So warm and calm,
As the shimmering droplets drop gently down.

As days pass by, I'm lonely,
As night falls, I'm sad,
As morning begins, I'm happy.

My friends come round,
The house becomes so cheerful,
But when they go, it's quiet.

The dark, dim corners
Look as though ghosts are lurking,
The wallpaper so dull and white,

It looked as if bugs were creeping to and fro.

*Samantha Bayly  (11)*
*Heathfield Community College*


## IF I WAS . . .

If I was a flower, I would be a shiny sunflower,
If I was a sandwich, I would be a chicken with cucumber,
If I was a car, I would be a sporty Lotus,
If I was a mammal, I would be a strong gorilla,
If I was a chocolate bar, I would be a scrummy Caramel,
If I was a tree, I would be a great oak,
If I was a racket, I would be a badminton racket,
If I was an animal, I would be a cheetah,
If I was an insect, I would be a whispery wasp,
If I was a colour, I would be rosy red,
If I was a letter, I would be the leader, 'A'.

*Dan Bates  (12)*
*Heathfield Community College*

## MY BEDROOM

As I wander into
This warm, cosy place,
I see junk!

All I can see is
Junk, it litters the
Room from top

To bottom with
Clothes, books, games
And lots of boxes,

But still it is warm
And snug with the
Sunlight shining in.

I like my room.

*Jack Farley  (11)*
*Heathfield Community College*

## IF I WAS A . . .

If I was a chocolate bar, I would be a bar with a caramel filling,
If I was a car, I would be a bright red Ferrari,
If I was a gun, I would be a lethal bazooka,
If I was a tree, I would be a great oak,
If I was a book, I would be a book on adventure,
If I was a colour, I would be fiery red,
If I was a sport, I would be the quick-fire game of tennis,
If I was the weather, I would be the happy sun.

*David R Thompson  (12)*
*Heathfield Community College*

## OBLITERATED

I can't sleep, it's as if someone is trying
Frantically to keep me awake.
I'm in the darkness, just lying here
Half asleep, but still awake . . .

Hijacked plane, no one is aware,
Flying low, the plane is creeping nearer,
With its eye on the victims,
The innocent human beings.
The impact, the smell of burning,
Rubble falling, men and women run.
Dubiety, disbelief and confusion.
The repulsive smell of death filling the air,
Dust, smoke and fire,
Massive clouds of dust immerse everything
As people run for cover, shrieking in anguish and grief.
I've given up, it's no use. I'm so tired, I can't sleep.

I lean over and turn on the light, it floods in
As if the room and I have never seen it before.
My eyes pound. The serenity has gone.
Obliterated forever.

*Kirsten Read  (13)*
*Heathfield Community College*


## WINTER

Winter is coming! Fierce winds blow.
Winter is here! It's started to snow.
My face and hands have gone numb,
My fingers have swollen like plums.

As we scoop up snow from the garden,
We fetch some carrots for our snowmen.
We go inside to a blazing fire.
Warm it is, a feeling I admire.

I can smell the wood burning,
The fire is crackling,
Sparks are flying.
I love winter.

*Sarah Sheriden  (12)*
*Heathfield Community College*


# MY RABBIT, COCO

I remember hiking up the mountainous steps,
(I was only three or four, remember) to reach Coco's run,
I would climb the path and walk to the run.

I would climb in to greet him and play.
Coco was a bit of a bully and a bruiser,
He liked to boss my guinea pig, Hamish, around as well!

I remember his delicate black coat,
I also admired the brown spot on his nose.
Coco got his name from his feet which were chocolate brown.

When we moved house, I realised Coco was old.
Even when he was old, he was still a bully.
I remember Coco was bossy also.

When Coco was old, he became more subdued,
Hamish became braver and I started my Christmas phase.
The year went by and Coco went blind.

My mum took Coco to the vet's before school, I remember.
When I came back, I was told he had been put down.
Coco was buried at the bottom of my Nana's garden.

I will always remember Coco and he will always
Stay in my heart with his own special place.

*Matthew Brooker  (11)*
*Heathfield Community College*

## MY HIDEAWAY

Under the bridge I hide away from
All the madness of my mum and
The booming of my brothers.

As I clamber and crouch under
The sturdy bridge and the
Splashing, tapping raindrops

I peep from underneath and
Peer at the grey sky,
Wondering if I should enter my steaming house.

As I creep and crawl through
The dripping hedges and the winding trunks,
Squirrels jump from tree to tree.

I'm getting closer and closer to all the madness.

*Jodi Males  (11)*
*Heathfield Community College*


## IF I WERE

If I were a gem, I would be a sparkling crystal,
If I were a sport, I would be energetic volleyball,
If I were an animal, I would be a posh poodle,
If I were a car, I would be a Porsche,
If I were a planet, I would be Saturn,
If I were a tree, I would be a willow next to a river,
If I were a vegetable, I would be a fluffy baked potato,
If I were a sweet, I would be a marshmallow.

*Kerrie Wickham  (12)*
*Heathfield Community College*

## AUTUMN

The leaves are changing to orange, yellow and red,
The toadstools are starting to poke their heads through the moist soil.
I pick up the chestnuts to roast on our open fire.

The red squirrels are busy looking for nuts
To store for the long, cold winter ahead.
The birds feast on the last of the blackberries.

The wind whistles through the trees causing the leaves to rustle.
The dogs crunch the fallen leaves as
They chase a deer through the woods.

I wish I could curl up in my
Lovely warm bed and hibernate all winter.

*Nicola Milton  (11)*
*Heathfield Community College*


## WHAT DID I SEE?

I saw a girl flying in the sky,
I saw a peacock giving a sigh,
I saw an elephant fanning out his tail,
I saw a fish drinking out of a pail,
I saw a builder in the water,
I saw a duck making bricks and mortar,
I saw a heron eating duck feed,
I saw a glue stick start to bleed,
I saw a giraffe go all sticky,
I saw a blue tit with a long neck, all spotty.

*Gabrielle Stern  (11)*
*Heathfield Community College*

## SIRENS

My head hits the soft, feathery pillow.
The lights are fading, casting shadows along the house.
In the hush of the room I alone am there.
I begin to fall asleep.

The plane circles the vast structure.
The people below, their mouths agape, watch the horror unfold.
The fireball fills the blue sky with smoke.
Men and women shriek and cry out, running instinctively.
They jump from the tower, on fire, killing themselves rather than
                                        being burnt alive.
Curses ring out among the tears of anguish.

Thick, dark smoke pours out of the smashed windows, like a
                                        black snake.
Dust and smog gather over Manhattan,
Sirens blare out as they wind their way through the city.
With an almighty, shattering crash, the building begins to buckle,
Debris showers the streets and the scurrying people.
The first tower folds like a piece of paper and
Masses of concrete and metal plunge to the ground.
Rescue workers stare up to see the rubble hurtling towards them . . .

With a start, I wake up.
The radio wails like a siren, telling me to get up.
The glint from the early sun makes sleepy shadows appear,
I leave the warmth of the bed and make my way into the bleak,
                                        new day.
The siren fades to leave me alone in my world, my own world.

*Helen Miller  (14)*
*Heathfield Community College*

## ANOTHER DAY!

The rumble in the sky sends lots of heads to look up.
Dark, thick, evil-smelling smoke starts pouring out of the building,
Innocent people fly like birds out of the windows,
Knowing they are going to die.
People run and scream as the hard, heavy rubble
Suddenly starts to fall, fall to the ground.
The sound of people's helpless screams pierce the air.

Sitting there in the dull, boring classroom,
I listen to my teacher blabbering on and on.
As she speaks, she looks at us with those eyes,
Those eyes of evilness.
Looking around, I notice that everyone looks
As bored as a lemon sitting in a fruit bowl.
My friend looks over to me and smiles slowly,
As if to say, 'I wish I was watching EastEnders.'

The smell of dust and smoke makes people cough, choke
                                    and suffocate.
Sirens of police cars and fire engines are barely
To be heard because of the commotion.
Firemen gaze with horror at the collapsing building,
Thinking, 'Oh my God!'
The smoke and dust are now so thick and so dark
You can hardly see a thing within it.

The teacher strides out of the classroom like a soldier obeying an order,
She comes back with a pile of textbooks,
Everyone moans, like a swarm of bees.
The bell rings, breaking the silence of the room,
There's a sigh of relief as we pack our things away.
The teacher sighs with disappointment and dismisses us.

*Rachael Hemsley  (14)*
*Heathfield Community College*

## THE YEAR 2000

This year, millennium, was the best,
Everybody joined in from east to west.
We had new stuff like the London Eye,
That was fun, but 400ft high.
My friend called AJ took me there,
Even though I was scared.
The Millennium Dome was also made,
Instruments and other things were played.
Some of it was, well, quite poor,
Even though a JCB broke in against the law.
The Olympic Games were a very big event,
They all trained hard before they were sent.
There was loads of bombing in Israel,
Will peace ever really prevail?
The petrol crisis stressed us all,
No one knew when the price would rise or fall.
Most people escaped those terrible floods,
They made the ground all covered in mud.
And now me and our best ever year,
For some people this ended in floods of tears.
Many schools had their Christmas plays,
People kept clapping for days and days.
Everyone will remember this millennium year,
We leave it now with great joy and cheer.

*Matthew Farmer (11)*
*Heathfield Community College*


## BOWLS

The sky was blue and the birds were singing in the nearby field.
Behind me, I heard the skis sliding smoothly down the slope,
A rush of wind brushed past my face.
The long winding road gets eaten up by trees
Which are like soldiers standing to attention,
To either side, the rocks tower over me reaching for the sky.

Out in the woodland there is a place that has all the activities
you can dream of.
There are people climbing up the rocks like monkeys swinging
through the jungle.
I feel frightened as the wave rolls over me and I
Look down from the forty foot zip wire!

*Aran Caldwell (11)*
*Heathfield Community College*


## DANGER!

I'm in the science block, the bell rings,
It's break next, everyone runs down the stairs,
It's like a stampede.
Why are we running? There's no danger.
What would it be like if there was?
I'm glad I can't imagine . . .

Just a normal day at the office would turn into a global tragedy.
Meanwhile, horrified civilians are told they're about to die.
A sound like a bomb goes off, a tower is left in flames,
Terrified workers run down the stairs
While courageous firefighters run up.

A second plane crashes.
An accident? Not now it isn't.
The towers collapse live on television throughout the world.
People run in horror from the falling cloud of dust,
Half of Manhattan is covered in debris.
The rescue workers search tirelessly for survivors in the
scorching rubble,
Some families reunited, others separated.
The skyline left destroyed, as are thousands of lives.
The rescue workers finally destroy the remains
And any hope of survivors is lost.

*Matthew Dalton (13)*
*Heathfield Community College*

## WHY?

Sitting at the dining table,
My family to my right,
My friends to my left,
My family felt for them.

The plane collided with the towers,
Hot air rushed towards the ground,
People running for their lives,
People screaming for help.

We apologised,
It's not fair when you can't move,
But it happens and
We have to get on with life.

People ring their families from the plane,
They are petrified at what is going to happen.
Why did it happen? We know.
Who did it? We are going to find out.

*Anna Holoway  (13)*
*Heathfield Community College*




## THE JOURNEY

The journey is a short, but busy ride,
We pass the many children walking home,
Chattering about the day we had,
We turn on the radio . . .

Faces of disbelief all round
As the plane flies into the tower,
Flames break out and chaos arrives,
The noise is terrifying.

Millions standing by, helpless,
New York's landscape changed forever,
So many questions, but no answers,
All that is left is the rubble of the two towers.

My favourite song comes on the radio,
We pull into the driveway.
Home at last,
Safe and happy.

*Katie Holmes  (14)*
*Heathfield Community College*


# UNTITLED

When we climbed up the hill,
We were worried we were going to get lost
Amongst the trees and leaves.

Like a massive green wall, they went for miles,
North and south beyond, swaying
Under their roof of branches.

The trees fluttered all over the place,
The songs of birds flew from the treetops,
Talking to each other constantly.

Each one gleaming with the light
Of the sun and the gleam of the trees,
Plus ourselves, so minutely small.

We thought we were helpless.

*Simon Gayton  (11)*
*Heathfield Community College*

## Out Of India

Out of India of the bright coloured saris,
Out of India of the dust and poverty,
Out of India of the dark grey elephants,
Out of India of the praying Hindus,
Out of India of the dancing ladies,
Out of India of the bright coloured bhindis.

Out of China of the flooded paddies,
Out of China of the stir-fried noodles,
Out of China of the brightly coloured dragons,
Out of China of the different hats,
Out of China of the long bamboo shoots,
Out of China of the green tea.

Into Australia of the coloured boomerangs,
Into Australia of the bouncing kangaroos,
Into Australia of the surfing competitions,
Into Australia of the smoky barbecues,
Into Australia of the shy koala,
Into Australia of the bush land.

*Rebecca Dryer  (11)*
*Heathfield Community College*


## Football Match

I can imagine the crowd ranting and raving
As I get off the train and head to the stadium.
The players come on full of football cravings,
And here comes the star known as 151.

The game kicked off, dead on three,
The ball went to one goal, to the other.
The game finished, a draw as it deserved to be,
Everybody cheered, including me and my brother.

I had a great time and I don't want to leave,
I'll come back soon when the season starts.
As I got on the train, I was pushed and heaved,
My God, I'd better protect my jam tart.

*Michael Lynch  (12)*
*Heathfield Community College*


## GOING TO SCHOOL

Out of the house, onto the bus,
Out of the house, onto the cigarette-smelling bus,
Out of the house, onto the tall double-decker bus,
Out of the house, onto the busy bus with people chewing gum,
Out of the house, onto the stripy bus with an annoyed driver,
Out of the house, onto the old 269 bus.

Off of the bus, into the school,
Off of the bus, into the huge school,
Off of the bus, into the busy school with hundreds of children,
Off of the bus, into the crowded school,
Off of the bus, into the school with long corridors and hundreds
                                              of classrooms,
Off of the bus, into the school with hundreds of teachers to boss
                                              us about.

Out of the corridor, into a lesson,
Out of the corridor, into a lesson that smells of work and writing,
Out of the corridor, into a boring maths lesson,
Out of the corridor, think, think, what's the answer?
Out of the corridor, remember not to shout out,
Out of the corridor, the bell goes,

I jump up and shout, 'Wahoo!'
It's the end of the week, now I can relax,
Then the teacher looks at me.

*Jenny Partridge  (11)*
*Heathfield Community College*

# OUT OF THE AEROPLANE

Out of the aeroplane, all stuffy and hot,
Out of the aeroplane, no time to stop,
Out of the aeroplane, with an uncomfy chair,
Out of the aeroplane, with recycled air,
Out of the aeroplane, with a duty-free shop,
Out of the aeroplane, with a skip and a hop.

Into the airport, all happy with joy,
Into the airport, as I push past a boy,
Into the airport, all different faces,
Into the airport, with all different races,
Into the airport, the heating feels on,
Into the airport, our bags weigh a ton.

Into the traffic, busier than we thought,
Into the traffic, slowly so we don't get caught,
Into the traffic, home we go,
Into the traffic, slow, slow, slow,
Into the traffic, driving is a bore,
Into the traffic, the tyres must be sore.

*Lucinda Palmer  (11)*
*Heathfield Community College*


# MY HOLIDAY TO FLORIDA

One time I was going abroad,
The very best time to be had by all.
Finally we got on the plane,
Florida, here we come. Hooray!

We soon got off the plane,
Off to the hotel,
I hope we enjoy our stay in Orlando, Florida!

On the way home,
I remember everything.
Dash the dolphin's cheeky smile,
Animal Kingdom too!

*Samantha Holmes  (11)*
*Heathfield Community College*

## A WALKER'S NIGHTMARE

All is silent,
All is still,
Nothing moves on the grassy hill.

Suddenly from nowhere,
As it seems,
People come rushing out from the trees.

Six hundred teenagers
Are all set free,
One of them (of course) happens to be me.

Grass is churned up,
Fields are turned brown
And stressed-out teachers are wearing a frown.

Wildlife runs,
Flees in despair,
Heathfield pupils walk on, unaware.

Cautiously, bees return to their hive,
As the next year of Heathfield
Starts to arrive.

*Joe Randall  (12)*
*Heathfield Community College*

## JOURNEY OF LIFE

When I was one,
I filled my tum.
When I was two,
I went to the loo.
When I was three,
I was climbing trees.
When I was four,
I was looking for more.
When I was five,
I was juggling knives.
When I was six,
I beat my brothers with sticks.
When I was seven,
I dreamed of Heaven.
When I was eight,
I was banging on the gate.
When I was nine,
I ate some pine.
When I was ten,
I made a den.
When I was eleven,
I went to Devon.
When I was twelve,
Forget it!

*David Radford  (12)*
*Heathfield Community College*


## THE WALK

All the kids setting off on a journey to Vines Cross,
Kids marching, sun's shining, birds are singing in the sky,
The fields are bumpy, lumpy and round, up ahead is no sound.
People are eating crisps and cakes and
Some kids are eating bars of cornflakes.
Vines Cross, quiet and peaceful, then invading people.

Mobile phones going off, teachers screaming, their ears are steaming.
The fields are churned and muddy,
And some people's bellies are chubby.
Everyone off again,
Neighbours saying 'I'm glad they're going.
They're noisy and a pain.'

*Elea Prior (12)*
*Heathfield Community College*


## ALONE

I step up, shaking with nerves,
My heart is thumping,
Excitement in the atmosphere,
Yet what could happen in space, alone.

Away from family, friends,
Though I've been training for months.
What if something goes wrong?
What if I panic?

A sickening shake, the engine screeches,
The force is unbearable, pushing me back.
I'm flying,
Further away from home.

As I travel, I think
That this should be a wonderful experience
And I fly so far into space,
I think still, what will happen?

I could have fame and
I've always wanted to be here,
So why do I feel this way?
Unending possibilities for good and bad.

*Felicity Green (11)*
*Heathfield Community College*

# First Day At New School

Travel, travel, travel by car,
Travel, travel, is it far?
Can we stop? Are we there?
Oh stop please, this isn't fair!

Here we are, here we are,
Oh, I knew it wasn't that far!
I wonder where we have to meet,
A teacher says, 'Over there is your seat.'

I walk down the corridor to find my class,
I walk in and am not last.
Break, lunch, then the last lesson,
I think geography is the next session.

Back home and homework to do,
Wait till next year and you'll have some too.

*Deborah Blanch (11)*
*Heathfield Community College*


# Hooray, The Happy Holiday!

Hooray! We've finished,
Packed and ready to go
Off to Center Parcs,
Excited.
Hooray! We've arrived,
What shall we do?
Look around, go for a walk,
Or a bike ride will do.

Hooray! We're here for the week,
Home from home to me.
Swimming, tennis, badminton,
It's all great fun for me.
Hooray! But not now,
It's time to go
Back home to Sussex,
But we'll come back soon.

*Darrel Harris  (11)*
*Heathfield Community College*

# MY POEM

When we arrived, I saw the sea which was green and blue,
Big pebbles that dug into our feet
And the sand was set and sticky, it felt like glue.

The sea looked as if the stars had fallen in,
Hundreds of pearls floating to the surface,
The reflection of the sun and thousands of pins.

The slushy sand oozing out of my feet,
Birds flying smoothly across the clear sky,
People getting burnt in the fearsome heat.

Children shouting, not wanting to go,
Waves crashing against my legs,
People kicking pebbles while walking very slowly.

I love this place so very much,
It clearly has Mother Nature's touch.

*Clara Tsang  (12)*
*Heathfield Community College*

## PLAYING IN THE WOODS

The home we lived in was called 'The Spinney',
Which contained a small wood
That was light in the winter and dark with leaves in the summer.

In the spring, the carpet of bluebells gave a wonderful scent
And gave cover for our games of hide-and-seek.
The winter often smothered our boots with mud.

The wonderful oaks towered into the sky
And the birds and squirrels nested happily in their heights.
The branches gracefully supported our rope swings.

You could hear the birds singing up high
And the grasshoppers clicking down low,
But lots of the time, my brother and sister screaming.

I loved this time, playing in the woods.

*Charley Burgess (12)*
*Heathfield Community College*

## THE JOURNEY

A long way to go,
I will always remember
Through the driving snow,
It was the middle of December.

In the old familiar town
My journey would end,
A long way to go
To meet my friend.

Struggling along,
Up and down hills,
So bitter and cold
And my back really kills.

Now at the end
Of this long, long walk,
We have a hot drink
And a nice friendly talk.

*Andrew Burnett (11)*
*Heathfield Community College*

## OUR RIVER

We scrambled down along the stream's grassy bank.
Yesterday's heavy rain had swollen the brook, beyond its normal level.
The opposite bank had been breached,
Allowing the water to flood the lower paddock.

The flood across the paddock had forced the two smaller ponies
To seek higher ground, under the oak trees.
Their heads hung low as the wind whipped through their ragged manes.
The golden brown leaves from the oaks blew around their legs.

The black-headed gulls, driven in from the coast,
Screamed as they flew low across the fields.
Their cries seemed to jostle with the deep, rushing, swirling wind as
It raged through the shaking branches of the threatened oaks.

Although the wind dragged at my hair and chilled my hands,
I felt exhilarated and alive.

*Lily Davis (11)*
*Heathfield Community College*

## MEMORY OF MY SWING

As I sat quietly on my swing in my back garden,
I swung so high, my stomach churned,
I pictured many hedges beyond, with fences all around them.

My swing was blue and yellow with a seat made of strong plastic,
Barriers around it so I couldn't topple,
It felt like a cosy armchair.

A bumblebee buzzing around,
Black, furry and yellow,
Antennae like microphones.

Over the fence I swung and saw the gardener
With his lawn mower, creating shapes like a zebra crossing.
I cried, Mummy came out and picked me up.

What a lovely hour,
But now it's time for tea.

*Samantha Edmeads (12)*
*Heathfield Community College*


## SPONSORED WALK

We started our walk through the church to the field,
We looked at the views that stretched far to the weald,
The munching and crunching was heard far and wide
As each of us took it all in our stride,

Which seemed like forever, we then reached a lane,
Our steps got much quicker for fear it might rain.
We thought it was time for a fight with some mud,
It dropped to the floor with a splat and a thud.

We at last reached the pub, it was now time to eat,
Just to sit down, take the weight off our feet.
A sip of a drink, a rest and a talk,
For only too soon we'd be back on the walk.

*Oliver Kench  (12)*
*Heathfield Community College*


## STAMPEDE

Sitting watching the clock, waiting for the bell,
Like a cat waiting to pounce,
Then it goes. People jump up around me,
Books being shoved in their bags,
Then we wait, we wait for silence and
The teacher's permission to leave.

Crash! Bang! Everyone looks around,
Tears of fright and shock.
People trying to help, but not sure how,
Trying to be useful, but not get in the way.
They wait for the fire brigade and the ambulances to arrive,
But it seems like ages until they do.

Ash falling like rain, covering everything and making it grey.
Parts of the building falling from the sky,
Screams coming from every direction.
A stampede coming out of the front door and going down the road,
Then it falls like a tower of cards that has just been breathed on.

Then there's a stampede for the front door,
Everyone's eager to get home.
Queues for the buses and engines starting up,
That sound like growling lions.
Slam go the car doors, then they're off.

*Claire Ashdown  (13)*
*Heathfield Community College*

## SIX MILES

Walking and getting tired already,
Still so far to go.
So much mud
And so many trees,
Finally lunch at the pub.
Eating quickly,
So, so hungry,
Ready to go once again.
Aching legs,
Bruised shoulders,
My bag getting heavier,
Blisters covering my feet.

But still I go on,
At least no rain,
Pain everywhere,
Eating chocolate,
Taking my mind off this,
Talking and joking to friends,
Avoiding both mud and poo,
Difficult I know.
At last we arrive,
It's all over.

*Bronwyn Powell (11)*
*Heathfield Community College*


## AMERICAN DEVASTATION

The first devastating terror hit the tower,
Down in flames, the States' glory and power.

The second hit, as crowds watched in fear,
Panicking and screaming, those who were near.

High in the clouds, shouting in grief,
Trading certain death with quicker relief.

More pain in the hearts of the people around,
As the towers hit the open ground.

After that day the countries unite,
To remember those people who died in the fight.

A day that we will always remember,
That day is the 11th September.

*Lynsey Coleman  (11)*
*Heathfield Community College*


## ALL AROUND THE WORLD

Into Spain with the hot sun overhead,
Into Spain, lying on a boiling sunbed,
Into Spain, placing a cool glass of water,
Into Spain, looking out to sea,
Into Spain, knowing I will be . . .
Into Spain . . . going, going, gone.

Out of Brazil, the football team scoring,
Out of Brazil, Argentina's weeping,
Out of Brazil, we're laughing,
Out of Brazil, we're saying our goodbyes,
Out of Brazil, leaving with happiness and joy.

All around the world, crying and weeping,
All around the world, shouting and cheering,
All around the world, lying and sleeping,
All around the world, drinking and eating,
All around the world, swimming and diving,
All around the world in a day!

*Dominic Cranfield  (11)*
*Heathfield Community College*

# MY POEM ON MY HOLIDAY

My mum woke me up on that special day,
We were going on holiday.
We lifted our bags into our car
And drove for an hour - it was quite far.
We got to the airport,
The plane so high and taut,
We went in and saw our gate,
Quick, hurry, we mustn't be late.
We waited and waited until we were allowed in,
We got there met an air hostess, she said her name was Lynn.
We sat at the back of the plane
And after eight hours, I was going insane.
We arrived in Florida glad and excited,
For the rest of our holiday we were all delighted.

*Sophie Jupp  (11)*
*Heathfield Community College*


# THE AVERAGE CLASSROOM

The board, the markers, the ballpoints and quills,
The papers, the documents, rubbers, pencils,
The blabbing disrupted by Janes, Jacks and Jills,
Disturbingly queer noises sounding very much like drills.

The educators, coaches, lecturers and tutors,
The work, the books, school rules and new laws,
The mistakes, faults, slip-ups, blunders and errors
Are all pointless objects which everyone ignores.

The bullies, the tyrants and the ruffians who jeer,
The fashionables, morons and the deaf who can't hear,
The skilful, attractive and the curious who peer,
Are all exceedingly bored by the dull atmosphere.

*Jonathan Parker  (12)*
*Heathfield Community College*

# WHAT AM I?

I am a walking pineapple,
Snuffling like a police dog
Looking for a victim.

When I'm scared,
My armour protects me,
I'm as thorny as an old man's beard.

My job is a coal miner,
Digging down in the dirt,
As muddy as a boot cleaner.

Tiny eyeballs,
Black, glassy marbles,
Spiky like forked lightning.

What am I?

*Helena Cole  (14)*
*Northease Manor School*


# ALLITERATION

One white water-logged wallaby,
Two tropical turtles were toddling along,
Three Thelmams thought their Thelmas were 'th'antastic,
Four fantastic families found fame,
Five funny families found their fishes,
Six sillies went swimming in the Shampoo Sea,
Seven snakes sneaked somewhere surprising,
Eight elephants entered the elephant kingdom,
Nine naughty nymphs knitted a nothing,
Ten tops turned and then topped over.

*Helen Hurst  (14)*
*Northease Manor School*

## A TERRIFIED TEAPOT

One wailing whale wished a weeping waffle,
Two taming tadpoles tap a topless tank,
Three thin thorns trick a thunder thief,
Four fluffy frogs found a filthy fly,
Five fizzy figures fiddle a fatty fin,
Six silly singing sisters slipped and were sick,
Seven sexy seagulls searched the seashore,
Eight electric eels embarrassed an elf,
Nine nobodies knew nothing,
Ten terrible tents terrified a teapot!

*Elliott Hutchings  (14)*
*Northease Manor School*


## TEACHERS

T   eachers are loud, twisted and cruel,
E   asily make us kids feel awfully small,
A   nd between you and me, their breath smells and
C   aution, their punishment is worse than death.
H   urry up, they cry,
E   very reply with a sigh,
R   est our soul if you dare to reply,
S   urely we should get them with an egg custard pie.

*Edward Harvey  (13)*
*Northease Manor School*


## ONE WHITE WASH, WASHED WHITE

One white wash, washed white,
Two tall twits talked to a toad,
Three thick thermometers thought they needed therapy,
Four fat fiddles fought for freedom,
Five fleas flattened from fright.

Six sick sticks sit sipping steaming soup,
Seven sleepy snails got slaughtered,
Eight eager elephants ate everything,
Nine neat newts never knew anything,
Ten torn towels told a telling tale!

*Joshua Penrose  (14)*
*Northease Manor School*


## ONE WIGGLY WORM

One wiggly worm whispered a wives' tale,
Two twits tripped over twins,
Three thick thugs thumped three friends,
Four frogs fought over ferns,
Five fishing fat females fought over fish,
Six small sausages simmered slowly,
Seven silly sisters sat singing,
Eight awful apes ate ants,
Nine new nits nipped Nelly,
Ten trees talked to Tom.

*Helen Gould  (14)*
*Northease Manor School*


## IN MY DAD'S POCKET

In my dad's pocket you would most probably find,
His car keys, a piece of tissue,
Some leftover sandwiches from long ago,
A small teddy that he has stolen from me,
His broken watch is still in there,
But you never know, maybe you will find some loose change,
And you never know what else might be in there . . .

*Alesha Good  (11)*
*Patcham House School*

# THE FROZEN MAN

The frozen man
So cold he was

Nearly a block of ice
I did imagine he was

From the great war
He also seems so poor

As if he had lost everything he owned
He lost his family and friends.

The trees cracked
Their fingers in icy winds

The frozen man looked
He wanted to come in to the snug house
At the heart of the town
And sit by the red, yellow and gold fire

I say
Let him in
Let him in
Of course I'd let him in.

*Claire Mansfield  (14)*
*Patcham House School*


# WHAT HAPPENED?

A black handbag,
Just been bought.

A mobile phone,
Just been used.

Party invitation,
To a fancy dress ball.

Snap of a boy,
Is it a lover?

Red on her hands,
Is it paint?

Torn up letter,
What did it say?

*Kate Evans  (14)*
*Patcham House School*

## THE FROZEN MAN

Out at the suburbs of town
Where fern trees grow

Amongst many others
In the cotton-like snow

Christmas lights twinkle
On the spiky tree

The screams for joy of people
Like fireworks in the midnight sky

Stockings hanging on fireplaces
But nothing for poor old Kit Wright

Poor old Kit Wright
All alone in the street at night

No wit's Christmas Eve
What will Kit Wright receive?

What!
What!
What!

*Kirstie Russell  (13)*
*Patcham House School*

## IN MY MOTHER'S POCKET

My mum's pocket is stuffed full of all sorts of things,
A screwed up shopping list,
Sticky chocolate wrappers,
Heavy keys,
Loose money,
Mobile phone,
An old purse,
Crumpled up tissues
And ten pound notes.
I think she ought to get rid of some of it.
She could give the ten pound notes to me!

*Craig Sweetman  (11)*
*Patcham House School*


## DANNY

D  angerous Danny,
A  lways ready for action,
N  o way to stop him,
N  ever get in his way,
Y  ou will wish you hadn't.

*Danny Wood  (12)*
*Patcham House School*


## FEARS

Frozen at the top of the stairway at night,
From the howls and screams below it could be a murder,
With his thin, broken fingers sitting in fear,
Shine with trace of a cold tear.

Suddenly the stairs start to creak,
Door opens, daddy-long-legs comes in, crawls up my leg,
I squash it with a nearby book,
A peek of a gun appeared,
Aimed at me and fired.

*Ryan Bull  (11)*
*Patcham House School*


## IT'S JUST THE WHEELCHAIR THAT'S DIFFERENT

People talk about me, not to me.
I have feelings just like anyone else.
I need people to talk to and friends.
My chair isn't me, it's just what I use to move around in.
Without my chair I would be sitting in the corner all alone,
With no way of moving.
Don't look at my chair,
Look at me!

*Stacy Struthers  (12)*
*Patcham House School*


## THE MONSTER

Scared at the top of the stairway at night,
From the sounds below a monster might bite,
With his sharp yellow teeth,
She curled up with fear,
Her dark eyes shine with the trace of a tear,
Creaking, coming up the stairs,
Nearer and *nearer* and *nearer* still,
I screamed and I ran.

*Natalie Homan  (11)*
*Patcham House School*

## TEACHERS NEVER UNDERSTAND ME

*Pupil*
Why do teachers pick on me?
I'm sweet
I'm good
I make people laugh
But why do teachers pick on me?

*Teacher*
You're bad
You make me mad
You wreck my lessons
You make me sad.

**Gez Faulkner  (13)**
**Patcham House School**


## JAMIE BRYANT

J    umping Jamie
A    thletic mad
M   arathon runner
I    ce skater
E    nergetic athlete.

B    asketball bouncer
R    owing champion
Y    acht sensation
A    rchery competitor
N    ascar racer
T    errific sleep!

**Jamie Bryant  (11)**
**Patcham House School**

## IT'S A HATEFUL WORLD

Why do people hate others?
Because of their skin,
Religion,
Disabilities?
Did something happen?
Are they scared they could end up the same way?
Did someone tell them something wrong?
People shouldn't be prejudiced.
No one has the right to hate anyone
Who is different to them.
Never judge anyone.
Everyone is the same on the inside.
Always get to know them,
You will find they are understanding, caring and kind.
Maybe you should give them a chance to be themselves with you.

*Rheana Roe  (12)*
*Patcham House School*


## GRAN'S POCKET

In my gran's pocket you would probably find,
A sample pack of porridge oats,
A lucky shamrock,
A leprechaun keyring,
A rusty glasses chain,
A four-leaf clover,
A bottle cork,
A photo of Jeremy Paxman,
And tapes of Mozart and Beethoven.

*Richard Poole  (11)*
*Patcham House School*

## THE FROZEN GIRL

Out at the edge of the wood
Where black trees are swaying

In the wind
Like monsters coming towards me

And hedges freeze
Their eyes staring at me

And the breath of sheep
Like a misty sea

Makes me cold
Like ice

I am walking alone
And trying to find my home.

*Alice Woodhouse (13)*
*Patcham House School*


## IN MY SISTER'S POCKET

Some old screwed up tissues
With goo all around
An ancient dried up pen
A black fingernail
A mouldy tooth
That's been there forever
And a rusty penny
A half-chewed lolly
With dust and hair on it
Some mushy sweets
Some white socks
That might be a year old.

*Joshua Good (11)*
*Patcham House School*

# HOW CAN A COUNTRY BE LIKE THAT?

Women fall, pick themselves up,
Another tear runs down their cheek.
The crack of the whip, a gun at their head,
How can a country be like that?

A deprived old lady, poor and frail,
Stumbles on rocks that cut her feet.
She's never hurt a single soul, kept her faith,
Yet still gets beaten with a stick.
How can a country be like that?

A woman shows her face, a young 17 year old,
With beautiful rosy lips and bright blue eyes.
No one can shut such a beauty out,
Her back beaten she showed her youth.
A hard bullet, another life gone.
How can a country be like that?

Second class citizens still humans yet another sex,
They have brought their children up.
To learn wisdom, fortune and faith,
More than what the men could teach,
For they have set an example to hurt, kill and punish women.
How can a country be like that?

If it is not racism then it's what sex you are,
In this world you cannot win,
But really how can a country be like that?
Poor defenceless women treated as slaves,
'Hide your face you shouldn't be a woman,'
I ask how can a country be like that?

*Emma Baker  (14)*
*Patcham House School*

# THE CONFUSED MAN!

Through the mist, a man marched down the murky paths,
where the quiet birds sing.
Raindrops pouring down his war bruised back,
not knowing where he is or who he is?
The *icy* wind piercing his coal-blacked face.
He carries on walking, locked in his own time-warped mystery!

*Sam Johnston (13)*
*Patcham House School*

# LEO

*Leos are faithful and trusting*
*Much to be embraced*
*By the arms of the embracing*

You may feel lonely this week
But remember you will find what you seek
You have many friends around you
And your family are there for you too

So remember to embrace those who embrace you.

*Kylie Mullock (13)*
*Portslade Community College*

# SCORPIO

This week you will come across a good job
Take the chance and you will come into a few bob.
It will be a bumpy road to success,
But in the end you will get what's best.
A fiery Leo will help you through
Your love will last, whatever you do.

*Tara Jones (13)*
*Portslade Community College*

# OB

There once was a lophead named Rob,
He was a wee little fellow with a rather large gob.
He had a job which was to collect a few bob
From various people, including a yob named Tob.
He had a precocious parrot named Ob,
Who belonged to a murderous mob,
Who particularly liked to eat corn on the cob.
Rob had a best friend named Bob,
Who was also a member of the murderous mob.
Ob and Bob had a mate named Tob,
Who was also a member of the murderous mob,
But Ob's and Bob's mate Tob was not a friend of Rob,
And despite the fact that Rob was a
Non-member of the murderous mob,
They all really enjoyed watching Pob!

*Daniel Harris & Sohrob Kamali*
*Portslade Community College*


# AQUARIUS

Don't spend what you haven't got,
You could just lose this silly plot.
Put cash away for a rainy day and it will be sunshine all the way,
Put the whole amount into an account.

Travel tomorrow, *I said tomorrow,*
Then you will have no horrific sorrow.
Something big will happen soon,
Moving house or visiting the moon.

*Blake Mahin (14)*
*Portslade Community College*

# FORECAST FOR THIS WEEK

Your forecast looks rather bleak,
You've got bad luck for the next two weeks.
You will lose someone dear,
And danger lurks near.
Beware the mysterious man!
Avoid him if you can.
If he enters your life,
Misfortunes will be rife.
However, there is good luck ahead,
Your lucky colour is red.
Take a great risk,
Go on, but be brisk.
The answer to whatever you seek
Is written in the stars next week.

*Marcel Armour  (13)*
*Portslade Community College*


# THE TANK

Rattles like a rattlesnake,
Sounds like a firecracker,
Fires like a cannon,
As heavy as a whale
And as big as an elephant.

*Joe Dunk  (12)*
*Portslade Community College*


# SUPERSTITION POEM

Never cross on the stairs,
Always be aware.
Bless you when you sneeze
And always choose sevens and threes.

Cross your fingers and toes
Always wrap up when it snows.
Never walk under a ladder or you'll have bad luck,
And in the mirror never pose.

*Gemma Francis  (13)*
*Portslade Community College*


## PISCES

You will incur a great expense
Luck will be on the way in job and love
From someone you know you hate
Find out before it is too late.

*Katie Salanson  (12)*
*Portslade Community College*


## HOROSCOPE, ARIES

Aries are confident, quick and dynamic,
You will risk all for fun.
This Saturday, you will find your dream
And make it on your own.
At work, someone will call your phone
And instantly you will click.
You will then meet up and go see a flick.
Money will be just the same,
As if you were playing a game.
You have great health, which will also help,
And so you will yelp to the sky,
How lucky am I!

*Sinead Heaney  (12)*
*Portslade Community College*

## LONELY HEART

Fun loving troll, dirty and smelly
With damp slimy skin, and a big hairy belly.
Nice muddy fingers and grubby wet toes,
Hot steamy breath and rings through his nose.
With stains on his shirt and holes in his socks
Teeth that need cleaning and knots in his locks.
Tears in his trousers, and scuffs on his shoes
He's waiting to meet someone lovely, like you.
He likes dirty ditches and hiding in holes
Is certain to win when he fights other trolls.
Is very attentive, will woo you with roses,
Once he used them to pick both his noses.
He lives on his own in a dark stinking pit.
Oozing with slime and covered in spit
Now feeling lonely, he hopes there's a chance
He can meet someone similar for fun and romance.

*Hannah Wheatley (13)*
*Portslade Community College*


## THE VIRGO

Next week the blue moon will bring you luck
For your full self will appear,
Bright, loud and cheerful you will control the streets
But as the sun rises you should fear
As Mars mixes with Venus, you will fill with emotion.
Relationships will be at their worst,
But remember friends are just around the corner,
You feel comforted and safe, this will be a first.
As the week moves on, a positive flow runs through you
And you can stand up to your phobia.
And at the end of the week you will feel like a king.

*Anna Bourne (13)*
*Portslade Community College*

## WELCOME TO THE HAUNTED HOUSE

Step in through the rusty gates
be as quiet as a mouse.
We're going to sneak and take a peek
inside the haunted house.

Witches creep whilst the skull and bones peep
look behind you . . .
Can't let them find you.

Wizards making spider pies
it's good for a Hallowe'en surprise.
Mummy's making whilst the werewolves taking
it ain't as bad as vampires baking.

Now let's get out and run for the van
be as quiet as a mouse.
Tiptoe out whilst you still can
escape from the haunted house.

*Anja Howell  (13)*
*Portslade Community College*


## CATS AND DOGS

Cats, cool as ice
As suave as a swan
As brave as a boxer
Cats, like a loveable lion

Dogs, dirty as a dump
As loyal as a leopard
As cute as a kitten
Dogs, like a huggable hippo.

*Katherine Woodford  (12)*
*Portslade Community College*

## ZODIAC SUPERSTITION

| | |
|---|---|
| Aquarius: | Touch wood to keep your luck |
| Pisces: | A black cat brings good luck |
| Aries: | Looking over your shoulder brings a ghost |
| Taurus: | Breaking a mirror brings seven years bad luck |
| Gemini: | Never cross on the stairs |
| Cancer: | Keeps a horseshoe upwards |
| Leo: | Salute when you see a single magpie |
| Virgo: | There's a pot of gold at the end of the rainbow |
| Libra: | Cross your fingers and toes |
| Scorpio: | 'Bless you' when you sneeze |
| Sagittarius: | Do not walk under a ladder |
| Capricorn: | Choose sevens and threes. |

*Kirsten Harber (13)*
*Portslade Community College*


## ZODIAC POEM

*Sagittarius*

Money is not your concern this week
So channel your energy into the health you seek.
Too many things is often the case,
So slow down, come on, it's not a race.

*Virgo*

Get up Virgo, go with the flow,
Love could be coming, you never know.
Financial commitment could cause distress
So be tactful, try to spend a little less.

*Jade Doherty & Roxanne Gregory (14)*
*Portslade Community College*

## MISSION X

*Go, go, go!*
Keep down!
Move to the right,
Watch your step,
Tank at 3 o'clock.
Medic, medic,
Man down, man down!
*Attack!*
No mercy,
Rapid fire,
Sniper's on the hill, take him out.
Grenade him now.
Check the bunker,
Clear,
Enemy suspected.
*Incoming!*

*David Miles  (13)*
*Portslade Community College*


## A RHYME POEM

Put me on an island where the boys are few
Put me amongst the most vicious lions in the zoo,
You can put me on a tricycle and
I'll never fall off,
But whatever you do, don't put me
With a moaning Goth.

Goths are strange
Goths are odd
They're so weird
They always nod!

*Zoe Squires  (13)*
*Portslade Community College*

# A CHILD'S NIGHTMARE

I had a scary dream last night,
It really gave me quite a fright.
Now I shall tell you what I saw
It might make you faint on the floor.

At first there were bats everywhere,
They did really give me a scare,
Second I saw ghosts and mummies,
It was funny because they had no tummies.

Then I saw witches on their brooms,
Plummeting towards Earth to their dooms,
Then I saw a haunted house
It was owned by a giant mouse.

Please somebody wake me up,
And then with a bit of luck,
I shall wake up back in my bed,
Away from bats and away from the dead.

*Natalie Matthews  (13)*
*Portslade Community College*


# DESTINY'S DECISION

Your forecast this week looks rather good,
However beware because there could
Be a surprise around the corner,
Love, money or maybe a mourner.

The number four is relevant this week,
Open the door and find what you seek,
Love, money, health or work,
Or something else that may want to lurk.

Your lottery chance looks good this week,
Your gambling chance has reached its peak,
But watch your back, don't get too greedy,
Maybe donate some and give it to the needy.

*Luke Thompson  (13)*
*Portslade Community College*


## THE TOAST GHOST

A hungry ghost longed for some toast,
'I eat a loaf' he'd often boast.
Words he longed for someone to utter
Were 'Here's some toast and plenty of butter.'
The ghost lived in a ruined house
In which he shared with a little mouse.
It squeaked no more, don't even look,
There is no cooker, nor a cook.

The ghost despaired 'What shall we do?'
The mouse replied 'If I were you . . .
I'd seek a cafe or a restaurant
And ask them to make you the toast you want.'
The ghost found the perfect spot,
He dreamed of toast, lovely and hot.
He waited for the cafe to close
Whilst the smells of toast teased his nose.

He went inside and found the kitchen
For buttered toast the ghost was itching.
Then something white behind the door
Floated softly to the floor.

*Hannah Chatfield  (14)*
*Portslade Community College*

## HALLOWE'EN

On Hallowe'en all the bats come out,
To fly around and freak us out.
Pumpkins glimmer in the dark,
And shadows move about like darts.

Trick or treaters roam the streets,
Hunting round for sweets and treats.
Witches flying up and down,
Never touching holy ground.

Haunted houses below the moon,
An eerie, dreary look of gloom.
Wizards' spells are extra strong,
Bloodstains now will never be gone.

Cobwebs stuck round everywhere,
Sure to give everybody a scare.
Ghosts flying up high in the sky,
A creepy glowing green cat's eye.

Skeletons hanging up on their own,
A haunting, scary, long deep moan.
Oh Hallowe'en this spook-filled night,
Guaranteed to give everyone a fright.

*Katrina Tognazzi  (13)*
*Portslade Community College*

## BURNING BRADLEY

Wanted - Burning Bradley
Big nose, with small eyes.
Thin body, fat thighs.
Black hair going grey,
His girlfriends would never stay.
Goes round with a dog called Dre.

Wanted - Burning Bradley
Robbed a bank for its chairs,
A house for its teddy bears.
A horse for its shoes,
A cow for its moo!
And a baby for its candy too!

Wanted - Burning Bradley
If found, don't be scared.
Just grab him, but be prepared,
For he pulls out a flame
Thinks it's a game,
And burns all the hairs off his
Great Dane.
That's why he is called - Burning Bradley.

*Elissa Owen  (13)*
*Portslade Community College*

## THE DIFFERENCES BETWEEN STAR SIGNS!

Virgo:   Shy, modest and tactful.
Aries:   Confident, quick and risky.

Aries:   *'Hello!* How was your week?'
Virgo    'Well . . . it was a nice quiet week. I didn't have much to do!
         How about you?'

Aries:   *'Argh* . . . I thought you would never ask! I . . . went to Africa
         in a canoe and nearly got eaten by a shark, but of course I got
         away. Then I went through the jungles swinging from trees to
         stop the man-eating elephants from getting me! After then I
         was chased by a group of wild cave men. I found out that my
         canoe had been smashed up, so I had to swim back from
         Africa. But that's about it for my week, not much really!'

Virgo:   'Did you really do all of that?'

Aries:   'Well . . . I did most of it. Like the bit about the cavemen and
         the man-eating elephants.'
Virgo:   'I haven't heard of man-eating elephants!'

Aries:   'I might have made that tiny little bit up then.'
Virgo:   'And cavemen, do they still exist?'

Aries:   'Course they do! Or they might. No they don't!'
Virgo:   'So you made it up then?'

Aries:   'Well in a way. Yes, yes I did!'
Virgo:   'So what did you do with your week then?'

Aries:   'Sat around watching television. *But!* I did save the world.'
Virgo:   'I bet you did too.'

*Jade Baker (14)*
*Portslade Community College*